CONTENTS

Published 2010.
Pedigree Books Ltd, Beech Hill House,
Walnut Gardens, Exeter, Devon EX4 4DH
books@pedigreegroup.co.uk / www.pedigreebooks.com

JAMES CAMERON'S

AVATAR™

£7.99

WELCOME
TO THE WORLD

Welcome to Pandora, mysterious moon of Polyphemus. As Colonel Quaritch would say, 'you're not in Kansas anymore'.

Jake Sully, former US Marine and reluctant participant in the Resources Development Administration's Avatar Program has travelled five years, nine months and twenty two days, to get to this backwater of the universe, simply to earn enough money for the operation to repair his severed spinal cord. He is enriched in a different way, however, as he experiences an unforgettable world light-years away from everything he has ever known.

Pandora is a fascinating, primal and terrifying destination. Even from orbit the scope of flora present on the surface indicates a planet brimming with life and up close the landscape is a visual feast. Huge swathes of rainforest extend as far as the eye can see and the vista is punctuated with jutting volcanoes, dramatic waterfalls, huge rock formations and colossal trees.

Life on Pandora is treacherous for both the indigenous Na'vi, desperate to defend their way of life, and for the human colonists, employed to strip the land of Unobtanium. Huge deposits of this precious mineral lie buried beneath Pandora's surface. Put simply, the Na'vi are sitting on a fortune and the RDA is not about to leave Pandora empty handed.

If necessary, the company is more than willing to employ the military might of its security force to achieve its aims.

Luckily, a select group of scientists, brought in to gain the knowledge and trust of the Na'vi via the Avatar Program, have morals, ethics and a healthy respect for worlds other than their own. Employed to drive the Avatar grown from a DNA mix derived from the Na'vi and his murdered twin Tommy, Jake starts out as a gun-for-hire, motivated solely by the wish to regain the use of his legs. However, once he has experienced Pandora, he grows to love the place, culture and people and loses his heart to one individual in particular. In the end, he is faced with an unenviable choice. Either turn his back on all he has known, or sacrifice the chance to embrace a brand new life and love.

RDA SCIENCE:
EXPLORATION ON PANDORA

The scientists working out of Hell's Gate Colony are pioneering human exploration on Pandora. Their mission is to study the biology, geology and zoology of this Earth-like moon and specifically learn about the indigenous population, called Na'vi, via the Avatar DNA infusion program.

To date, studies have focused on the Omaticaya. However, there are known to be no fewer than seven clans on Pandora, including the Pa'li and Ikran Clans.

Leading botanists take samples and catalogue the many different flora on the planet. Exciting new species discovered and registered since the establishment of the program include: the Spore, the Warbonnet and the Shao Plant.

The planet's fauna is equally exotic. Zoologists have noted the lemur-like Prolemuris and the six-legged Direhorse, used by the Na'vi for hunting and transport.

RDA's science team, led by Dr. Grace Augustine, believes it is on the brink of discovering something unique within the biological make-up of the planet. A neural network based around an electrochemical communication between the roots of the trees, which the Na'vi are able to access.

NAME:
The Spore

NAME:
The Warbonnet

NAME:
The Shao Plant

8

THE AVATAR PROGRAM

Funded by the RDA, the Avatar Program is dedicated to the training, maintenance and assignment of the genetically cloned Human/Na'vi hybrid Avatar bodies, into which a select group of scientists can transfer their minds. Once inhabiting an Avatar, the scientist can then freely explore the harsh Pandoran environment and attempt to interact with the native Na'vi species.

This process involves mixing human DNA with the Na'vi DNA to create Na'vi bodies. The scientists then 'link' the human consciousness of the 'Avatar Driver' who contributed the human DNA, with the new Na'vi body. Appearing within the Na'vi body, the Driver's mind can move among the Na'vi beings while its human body rests in suspended animation in a link unit. This enables the scientists to gain an inside view of the Na'vi and their way of life that they could never attain as human beings.

The program is run from a section of Hell's Gate made up of the Bio-Lab, Link Room and an external Avatar Compound where Avatars can acclimatise to the Pandoran environment. There are recreational facilities for enhancing physical training of the Avatars and they are stored within the Compound when not in use.

Past initiatives to improve relations between the indigenous population and the humans on Pandora have included a school to teach English to the children of the Omaticaya Clan. This was spearheaded and run by Dr. Augustine (Head of the Avatar Program) until its recent closure.

DUAL
PLAT
FORM
PRECISION SCANNING

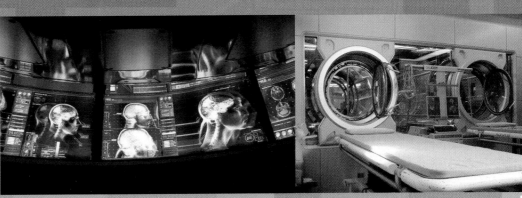

RDA SCIENCE: PERSONNEL PROFILES

NAME:
Jake Sully

PROFESSION:
Former US Marine - paralysed from the waist down during conflict in Venezuela.

CURRENT POSITION:
Employed by RDA's Avatar Program as an Avatar Driver.

SPECIFIC SKILLS AND PROFICIENCIES:
Advanced military training, combat skills, military tactics and strategy.

BASE OF OPERATIONS:
Earth, Hell's Gate Compound, Hometree.

PERSONALITY TRAITS:
Passionate, tenacious, moral, courageous.

STATUS:
Member of the Omaticaya Clan; Mated with Clan Tsahik-in-waiting, Neytiri.

QUOTES:
"There's no such thing as an ex-marine. You may be out, but you never lose the attitude."

"All I want is a single thing worth fighting for."

AVTR
PROGRAM

NAME:
Dr. Grace Augustine

PROFESSION:
Botanist, xenoanthropologist.

CURRENT POSITION:
Director of RDA's Avatar Program.

SPECIFIC SKILLS AND PROFICIENCIES:
Experienced Avatar driver, fluent in Na'vi, published author of 'The Na'vi'.

BASE OF OPERATIONS:
Hell's Gate Compound, Hometree, Site 26.

PERSONALITY TRAITS:
Determined, aggressive, practical.

STATUS:
Deceased. Shot by human security forces; her experiences were 'uploaded' into Eywa, also known as The Tree of Souls or The Mother Tree.

QUOTES:
"It's not our world. So keep safe and only collect information."

"I used to think it was benign neglect Parker, but now I see you are intentionally screwing me!"

AVTR
PROGRAM

NAME:
Norm Spellman

PROFESSION:
Xenoanthropologist.

CURRENT POSITION:
Scientist employed by RDA's Avatar Program;
Avatar Driver.

SPECIFIC SKILLS & PROFICIENCIES:
Textbook knowledge of multiple disciplines
including anthropology, linguistics, botany,
zoology and geology.

BASE OF OPERATIONS:
Hell's Gate Compound.

STATUS:
Remains on Pandora with a handful of
scientists in the Avatar Program.

PERSONALITY TRAITS:
Earnest, inquisitive, gregarious.

QUOTES:
"Who's Eywa? Only their deity. Their
Goddess. Made up of all living things.
Everything they know. You'd know this if you
had any training whatsoever."

AVTR
PROGRAM

NAME:
Dr. Max Patel

PROFESSION:
Supervisor of Avatar activity within Hell's
Gate Compound.

CURRENT POSITION:
Employee of the RDA.

SPECIFIC SKILLS & PROFICIENCIES:
Xenobiologist, neural networking.

BASE OF OPERATIONS:
Hell's Gate Compound.

STATUS:
Remains on Pandora to oversee the
abandoned Link Room in Hell's Gate.

PERSONALITY TRAITS:
Enthusiastic, moral, curious.

QUOTES:
"That's a gorgeous brain. Nice activity."

"Quaritch has taken over. He's rolling and
there's no stopping him."

AVTR
PROGRAM

RDA MILITARY:
MISSION STATEMENT

The Resources Development Administration, or RDA, is a powerful, independent, non-governmental organization which has the monopoly on all products shipped, derived, or developed from Pandora.

Pandora is rich in the mineral Unobtanium, which is a super-conductor at room temperature, making it a highly valuable commodity. In order to allow the RDA to safely mine this precious resource and ship it back for use on Earth, they have established a military presence on the planet.

Initially the role of the military was about providing protection for the mining operation and for the scientists and Avatar Program - hence the section name Security Operations or 'Sec-Ops'.

However, following the discovery of enormous deposits of Unobtanium beneath sites deemed sacred by the Na'vi population, priorities have changed.

RDA's military arm now supports the Avatar Program in as much as it allows them to gain access to the Na'vi and gain intelligence on their movements and way of life. However, if the Avatar Program fails to persuade them to relocate peaceably, Plan B is to use force in order to achieve this objective.

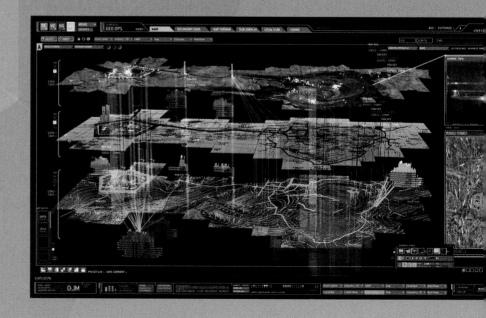

MIGHT AND MUSCLE

Security Operations (Sec-Ops) is comprised of former military personnel contracted from Earth now serving as a mercenary force on Pandora. It is headed by seasoned service-man Colonel Miles Quaritch. RDA Military's strength is significantly larger than most other military forces on Earth, and in terms of weapons technology it packs some real muscle.

The airfield sees constant traffic from large interstellar ships, interplanetary supply ships, shuttlecraft, assault ships and helicopters such as the SA-2 Samson and Scorpion Gunships. The Armour Bay houses the Amplified Mobility Platforms or AMPsuits. Life in Sec-Ops is tough, troopers arrive to a welcome briefing which leaves them in no doubt of the hostile environment which awaits them.

Colonel Quaritch is fond of telling new recruits that they may want to go to hell for some rest and retreat after a tour of Pandora. He hammers the point home by adding he will not succeed in keeping them all alive. The dangers of Pandora are reflected in the tongue-in-cheek tattoo art sported by many Sec-Ops troopers. Popular designs include 'If you can see Blue, he can see you', 'Too tough to die for the RDA' and 'Kill me now, but clone me first'.

KILL ME NOW BUT CLONE ME FIRST

13

RDA MILITARY: PERSONNEL PROFILES

RDA

NAME:
Colonel Miles Quaritch

PROFESSION:
Military contractor.

CURRENT POSITION:
RDA's Head of Security on Pandora.

SPECIFIC SKILLS AND PROFICIENCIES:
Advanced military training, combat experience, military tactics and strategy.

BASE OF OPERATIONS:
Hell's Gate Compound.

PERSONALITY TRAITS:
Aggressive, hard-edged, regimented.

STATUS:
Deceased. Killed by Neytiri, of the Omaticaya clan.

QUOTES:
"You are not in Kansas anymore, you are on Pandora, ladies and gentlemen, respect that fact every second of every day."

"I'm RDA's head of security. It's my job to keep you alive. I will not succeed - not with all of you."

RDA

NAME:
Trudy Chacon

PROFESSION:
Former US military services.

CURRENT POSITION:
Pilot in RDA Supply Fleet on Pandora.

SPECIFIC SKILLS AND PROFICIENCIES:
Skilled at flying a variety of vehicles.

BASE OF OPERATIONS:
Hell's Gate Compound.

PERSONALITY TRAITS:
Sarcastic, moral, brave.

STATUS:
Deceased. Killed in combat during her assault on Quaritch's Dragon Gunship.

QUOTES:
"I was hoping for some plan that did not include martyrdom."

"I didn't sign up for this!"

WEAPONS LOADING AREA IS RESTRICTED TO AUTHORIZED ARMOR BAY PERSONNEL

⚫⚫RDA

NAME:
Corporal Lyle Wainfleet

PROFESSION:
Former US military services.

CURRENT POSITION:
Contracted officer in RDA Sec-Ops on Pandora.

SPECIFIC SKILLS & PROFICIENCIES:
Advanced military training, combat experience.

BASE OF OPERATIONS:
Hell's Gate Compound.

PERSONALITY TRAITS:
Snide, aggressive, gung-ho.

STATUS:
Deceased. Killed by a rampaging Thanator during battle with the Na'vi.

QUOTES:
"Seen a lot of guys leave this place in a wheelchair. Never seen anybody show up in one."

"Let's bring the pain!"

⚫⚫RDA

NAME:
Parker Selfridge

PROFESSION:
Management.

CURRENT POSITION:
Executive Director of Hell's Gate Operations.

SPECIFIC SKILLS & PROFICIENCIES:
Supervises exploration and exploitation of Pandora's resources.

BASE OF OPERATIONS:
Hell's Gate Compound.

PERSONALITY TRAITS:
Arrogant, obsequious, materialistic.

STATUS:
Disgraced and shipped out on a shuttle for the five year journey back to Earth

QUOTES:
"This is why we're here. Because this little grey rock sells for twenty million dollars a kilo."

"Killing the indigenous looks bad, but there's one thing shareholders hate more than bad press - a bad quarterly statement."

120
Unm
unobtainium
$[Rn]5f^{14}6d^{18}7s^2$

PANDORA:
THE NA'VI

Pandora's indigenous population are the Na'vi, which translates in English as 'The People'. To date, it is the only known extra-terrestrial species found to have human-like consciousness and intelligence. At first sight this race of omnivorous hunter-gatherers may seem primitive - their technology and weaponry is equivalent to that seen on Earth during the Palaeolithic era. However, closer inspection reveals a sophisticated culture based on a profound spiritual connection to other life on their moon.

There are hundreds of disparate Na'vi clans on Pandora including the Omaticaya. Some are concentrated in the jungles and rainforests and, like the Omaticaya, live in huge, ancient trees they call Kelutral or 'Hometree'. Outlying clans have been detected in Pandora's coastal and mountainous regions as well as on the plains and in swampland.

Biological evidence would appear to indicate that, rather than arriving a long time ago from other star systems, the Na'vi evolved on Pandora, branching off from the common Pandoran evolutionary tree. This argument is based on physiological points including the presence of the Na'vi neural queue or hair braid, which is compatible with other Pandoran life forms, but is unique in that it is a single connection extending backward from the head, where most medium-large Pandoran creatures have two clusters within antennae.

The average Na'vi measures around 3 metres - 10 feet tall and weighs 286 lbs in Pandoran gravity, compared to 357 lbs in Earth's gravity. Females weigh slightly less as they are generally shorter and of lighter build. The Na'vi skeleton is reinforced with naturally occurring carbon fibre making them far less fragile than humans and despite their distinctive cyan-colouring - which earns them the nickname 'Blues' by human colonists - they are red-blooded.

NA'VI PHYSIOLOGY

NEYTIRI

Surprisingly, there are just as many striking similarities between the human form and physiology and that of the Na'vi, as there are differences. Here we take a close look at this incredible species.

Skin: Na'vi skin is smooth, iridescent, and cyan in color accentuated with slightly darker cyan stripes.

Facial markings: These are bioluminescent and glow when darkness falls. The body pigmentation patterns appear to follow the path of the circulatory or nervous system and aid in identification.

Hands & Feet: Four fingers on each hand and four toes on each foot, including opposable thumbs and big toes. Human created Avatars have five fingers and toes and their toes are non-opposable.

Ears: The ears of the Na'vi protrude prominently from the head. They are long and pointed and partially mobile, much like those of a bat. They are also translucent in certain light.

Nose: Flat and feral with two nostrils. The Avatars differ in that they have a more human-shaped nose with a ridge. Most other large Pandora creatures possess twin air intakes near the shoulder/breast bone for respiration and body temperature regulation.

Eyes: A single pair which are large, almond shaped and amber/gold in colour.

Neural Queue: This seemingly conventional long hair braid hides a complex system of neural tendrils ending in a nerve cluster, that can be connected to similar structures of other life-forms.

Torso: The neck is long and the body slender with wide shoulders creating a V-shaped upper back. Musculature is sharply defined giving them around four times the strength of the average human.

Limbs: The Na'vi are bipedal tetrapods. Like humans they have four limbs and move on their two legs. This singles them out from other Pandoran life forms, the majority of which are hexapods with six limbs.

Tail: Long and sweeping, but controlled like the limbs, it is primarily used as an aid for balance, but also helps express emotion.

PANDORA NA'VI: CLAN MEMBER PROFILES

NAME:
Neytiri

CLAN:
Omaticaya.

CLAN POSITION:
Daughter of clan leaders Eytukan and Mo'at,
Tsahik-in-waiting.

SPECIFIC SKILLS AND PROFICIENCIES:
Bow-hunting, Direhorse riding,
Banshee riding, dancing.

BASE OF OPERATIONS:
Hometree.

PERSONALITY TRAITS:
Daring, passionate, caring, loyal.

STATUS:
Mated to Jake before Eywa.

QUOTES:
"Sky People cannot learn. They do not See."

"Our Great Mother, Eywa, does not take sides.
She only protects the balance of life."

NAME:
Mo'at

CLAN:
Omaticaya.

CLAN POSITION:
Tsahik - Spiritual Leader, clan Matriarch.

SPECIFIC SKILLS AND PROFICIENCIES:
Ability to communicate with Eywa -
The Mother Tree.

BASE OF OPERATIONS:
Hometree, Tree of Souls.

PERSONALITY TRAITS:
Wise, direct, resilient, intense.

STATUS:
Remains Tsahik, Clan Matriarch of the
Omaticaya.

QUOTES:
"We have tried to teach the Sky People. It is
hard to fill a cup that is already full."

"If you are one of us, help us!"

NAME:
Eytukan

CLAN:
Omaticaya.

CLAN POSITION:
Olo'eyctan - Male Clan Chief.

SPECIFIC SKILLS AND PROFICIENCIES:
Excellent hunter, strategist.

BASE OF OPERATIONS:
Hometree.

PERSONALITY TRAITS:
Stern, commanding, contemplative.

STATUS:
Deceased. Impaled by wooden shards of Hometree, his spirit has joined with Eywa.

QUOTES:
"His alien smell fills my nose."

NAME:
Tsu'tey

CLAN:
Omaticaya.

CLAN POSITION:
Lead warrior, apprentice Olo'eyctan, intended to Neytiri.

SPECIFIC SKILLS AND PROFICIENCIES:
Ability to communicate with Eywa - The Mother Tree.

BASE OF OPERATIONS:
Hometree.

PERSONALITY TRAITS:
Stubborn, tense, honourable.

STATUS:
Deceased. Shot by a Sec-Ops trooper, and then fell to death during air battle to save Tree of Souls.

QUOTES:
"A rock Sees more!"

"Toruk Makto, I will fly with you."

INSIDE THE ICY CONFINES OF THE METAL CHAMBER, JAKE SULLY'S EYES FLEW OPEN AND HE DREW A LONG, RASPING BREATH: THE FIRST IN YEARS. WITH A JOLT THE CRYO CAPSULE WHERE HE LAY OPENED, EJECTING HIM SMOOTHLY INTO THE INTERIOR OF THE SPACECRAFT.

"You have been frozen cryogenically for five years, nine months and twenty two days," announced a medical technician. "You will be hungry. You will be weak. That is normal. If you feel nausea, please use the sacks provided."

Jake looked around at the rows of chambers that made up the cryo vault. His fellow passengers were easing themselves from their beds. He pulled himself up by his biceps and floated out to join them. In zero gravity his legs - paralysed during his service as a US Marine - did not impede him.

Jake was on his way to a new life, an unexpected new start on the moon Pandora. His identical twin brother Tommy, a scientist, had been killed in a robbery a week before he'd been due to ship out. The twins possessed the same genome so Jake had been offered the chance to step into Tommy's shoes. Attracted by the large pay packet and the chance to afford costly surgery to fix his severed spinal cord, he'd agreed.

Jake and the other passengers transferred onto a shuttle for the last leg of their journey to Pandora. They sat side-by-side as the crew chief yelled at them to put on the Exo Packs which would allow them to breathe in Pandora's toxic air.

"You lose that mask and you'll be unconscious in forty seconds, dead in four minutes," he shouted. "Let's nobody be dead today."

The shuttle descended through cloud. Jake got his first glimpse of Pandora through the window. Massive cliffs rose majestically from a vibrant green carpet of rainforest. There was just one blot on the landscape; the place where they were heading. Hell's Gate - the human colony - squatted in an ugly crater, a cluster of concrete and steel structures surrounded by razor wire fencing.

The passengers stood in line, duffle bags ready and masks clamped to their faces as the shuttle landed and its cargo ramp opened.

The arriving colonists ran in double time down the ramp, ordered to go directly inside. Jake transferred himself to his wheelchair and heaved his bag onto his back.

A couple of troopers from the Sec-Ops security force watched him roll out into the open with disdain.

The pair mocked him, one describing Jake as "Meals on wheels".

Jake ignored them and paused to watch a huge tractor roll into the compound. Its enormous tyres were pitted with blue arrows.

Inside, Colonel Miles Quaritch was giving his welcome briefing to the new arrivals. Jake joined them.

"You're not in Kansas anymore" Quaritch warned. "Beyond that fence every living thing that crawls, flies or squats in the mud wants to kill you and eat your eyes."

The room fell silent as Quaritch detailed the indigenous population of humanoids called the Na'vi.

"They're fond of arrows dipped in a neurotoxin and they are very hard to kill," Quaritch told them. "As head of security it is my job to keep you alive. I will not succeed. Not with all of you..."

>

When the briefing was over, Jake wheeled his way down a corridor. An eager young man ran after him.

"You're Jake right?" Norm gushed enthusiastically. "Tom's brother? Wow, you look just like him. I'm Norm Spellman; I went through Avatar training with him," Norm offered his hand.

Jake shook it warily as the pair entered the Bio-Lab. Norm introduced himself to several technicians while Jake rolled as if in a trance towards a large, hyperplex tank. A figure floated languidly inside. It looked like a man - a very large, very blue man, with black hair and a lemur-like tail. Blood circulated through a synthetic umbilical cord in its abdomen. As Jake watched, it turned in the amniotic fluid. Despite the feline ears and long snout its features were familiar.

"It looks like him," Jake murmured, thinking of his brother.

"No, it looks like you. This is your avatar now, Jake," Norm said, coming up behind him and staring at the synthesised version of Jake in the tank.

Doctor Max Patel walked over and welcomed Jake. He showed him how to start documenting everything via video log. Max explained the benefits of keeping the log; while it would be undoubtedly beneficial for scientific purposes, Jake's sanity was the main benefactor.

Jake thought he may as well start immediately, so he sat down and looked into the webcam attached to the nearest computer. With a cough he began talking...

"The concept is that every driver is matched to his own avatar so that their nervous systems are in tune. Which is why they offered me the gig, because I can link with Tommy's avatar..." he said.

Jake's monologue, though, was interrupted by a sudden commotion.

He turned to see the techs running into the Link Room which housed a dozen coffin-like link units. The lid of one chamber hissed open and Doctor Grace Augustine sat up and stretched.

"Grace Augustine is a legend," Norm explained, as Max led him and Jake into the Link Room. "She's the head of the Avatar Program, she wrote the book on Pandoran Botany."

Max introduced Norm to Grace.

"How's your Na'vi?" she asked. Norm responded with a fluent sentence in the alien language.

Still ignoring Jake, Grace advised Norm that he sounded a little formal, but his Na'vi wasn't bad.

"This is Jake Sully." Max prompted.

Grace's response was brusque. "Yeah, I know who you are, and I don't need you. I need your brother. You know, the PhD who trained for three years for this mission?"

Norm and Max looked embarrassed.

"He's dead," snapped Jake. "I know it's a big inconvenience for everyone."

"How much lab training have you had?" Grace asked.

"I dissected a frog once," quipped Jake.

This was too much for the scientist. She turned on her heel and strode out of the lab to find the colony administrator.

>

Administrator Parker Selfridge was trying out a new golf putter in the Operations Centre. He was not in the mood for complaints. "I need a researcher, not some jarhead dropout." Grace said.

"Lucky your guy had a twin brother, a Marine that we can use. I'm assigning him to your team as a security escort," said Selfridge, reminding Grace of her purpose - to gain the trust of the natives.

Then, grabbing a lump of metallic rock from his desk and waving it angrily at her, he reinforced the motivating factor behind their mission.

"Unobtanium! This little rock sells for twenty million a kilo. It's what pays for your science." he paused, composing himself. "Those savages are threatening our operation. We're on the brink of war and you're supposed to be finding a diplomatic solution. So use what you've got and get me some results."

Grace had no comeback, the discussion was over.

Next morning Jake and Norm reported for duty in the Bio Lab. Grace seemed delighted with Norm's five hundred and twenty hours of time spent linked to his avatar, but less than pleased when Jake told her he'd done nothing except read a manual.

"Tell me you're joking," she grimaced as she watched Norm and Jake climb into their link beds. As Jake hauled his inert legs onto the bed, Grace began pressing buttons.

"So you just figured you'd come out here to the most hostile environment known to man, with no training of any kind, and see how it went?" she asked.

"Maybe I was sick of doctors telling me what I couldn't do" he replied defiantly.

Grace finished adjusting biometric sensors and pushed Jake's head down into the gel pack lining his unit.

"Just relax and let your mind go blank. Shouldn't be hard for you," she said, slamming the hood, striding to her own unit and climbing in.

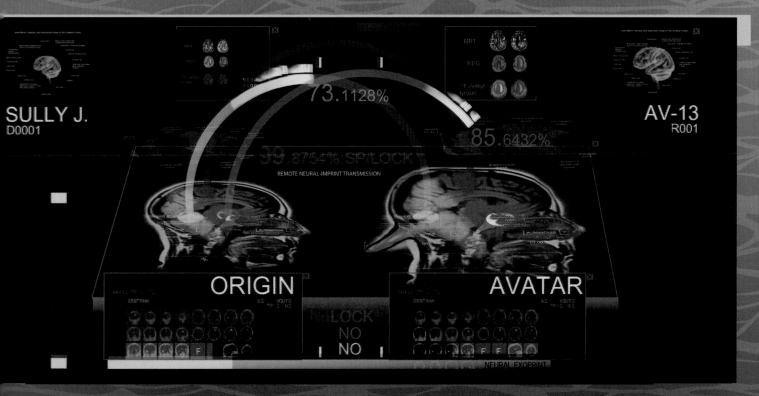

SULLY J.
D0001

AV-13
R001

73.1128%

85.6432%

99.8754% SP/LOCK

REMOTE NEURAL-IMPRINT TRANSMISSION

ORIGIN

AVATAR

LOCK
NO
NO

NEURAL EXOPRINT

There was a hum of activity. "Phase-lock ninety nine percent. Link is stable." announced one technician and with a zap and a fizz the link between Jake's brain and his dormant avatar was established.

Jake opened his eyes to see two blurry figures snapping their fingers before his face. Jake's vision sharpened and he saw two medical technicians fussing round him. They seemed smaller than before. He lifted his arms to see two huge hands wiggling blue fingers in front of him and stared in wonderment, barely aware of Norm's avatar beside him going through similar checks.

With a lurch he was up from the stretcher. A huge grin lit up his face as he felt the strength in his legs. The techs, looking nervous, urged Jake to sit down, but he ignored them.

"Guys, get him back on the stretcher." Max's voice was anxious through the loudspeaker.

Something like a blue tentacle curled round Jake's arm and he whipped round in alarm to find his tail swishing from side to side. With a 'swoosh' it swept a tray of instruments from a cart, sending them crashing to the floor.

"Sedate him." came the cry, but before the techs could fill their syringes Jake crashed out into the compound, tail protruding from his green gown, eyes blinking in the sunlight.

Feeling incredible, he began walking, jogging, and sprinting, laughing out loud as his new legs carried him through the undergrowth at breakneck speed. When his euphoria had worn off, Jake returned to the group, fully adjusted to his new body. With his first experience as an avatar over, Jake joined the other avatars to sleep in the compound.

"Lights out." ordered the avatar version of Grace as Jake studied the strange tentacles protruding from the end of his braided hair. He closed his eyes to make the journey back to his real body.

>

Next morning, a female pilot named Trudy approached Jake over breakfast and told him the Colonel wanted him in the Armor Bay. On the way there she filled Jake in on her role.

"I fly the science sorties and this here is my baby," she said, slapping the nose cone of her armoured helicopter.

"You guys are packing some heavy gear," Jake said, watching Wainfleet fix a machine gun to one side.

"That's because we're not the only thing flyin' around out there. Or the biggest," Trudy said, telling him she'd need him stationed on a door gun.

"I thought you'd never ask," Jake smiled.

The Colonel was bench-pressing huge weights in a makeshift gym area at one end of the bay.

"I pulled your record, Corporal," he grunted, sitting up and looking Jake in the eye. "I was in First Recon myself a few years ahead of you. Three tours in Nigeria, not a scratch. I come out here," he pointed to the three long scars marring his weathered face. "Day one."

The Colonel crossed over to a robotic AMP Suit and began climbing in.

"But you know what? I kinda like it," he grinned grimly. "Reminds me every day what's waiting out there."

Quaritch settled into the cockpit and flicked switches. As he did so, he gave Jake his frank opinion - that the Avatar Program is a joke, but the opportunity to have a recon Marine involved could generate useful intel. The AMP Suit roared to life as Quaritch inserted his arms into the controls.

"I want you to learn these savages from the inside, to gain their trust. I need to know how to force their co-operation. Or hammer them hard if they won't," he continued, assuring Jake he'd still be under Grace's control...at least on paper.

"You get me what I need, I'll see to it you get your real legs back!" he yelled, performing a couple of punches and making his robot's arms do the same. Jake smiled as he watched Quaritch effortlessly manoeuvre the two ton robot towards the exit.

After his talk with Quaritch, Jake reported to the Link Room ready for his first proper outing on Pandora in his avatar body.

"Just keep your mouth shut and let Norm do the talking," Grace warned, as she snapped the lid of his unit closed. Within minutes the avatar versions of Norm, Grace and Jake were in Trudy's helicopter flying towards the forest. Jake whooped with delight as they banked over a massive waterfall.

When they'd landed, the avatar trio made their way into the forest. The place was teeming with strange life-forms. Jake gripped his rifle as a monkey-like creature leapt from the bough of a tree up ahead of him.

"Prolemuris. They're not aggressive," Grace told him, lowering the nozzle of his gun and urging him to relax.

While Grace and Norm squatted to take samples from some roots, Jake wandered into a glade. He was amusing himself making enormous spiral plants to shut and vanish at his touch when an almighty roar chilled him to the core. A fearsome creature, like a rhino, but with six legs and a hammerhead loomed into view. A Hammerhead Titanothere. Jake raised his rifle.

Again, Grace stopped him, instructing him not to shoot or run. Instead she told Jake to hold his ground.

But Jake wasn't about to become the creature's lunch. As the Titanothere lowered its head and prepared to charge Jake rushed straight at it, screaming at the top of his lungs.

The beast stopped abruptly and retreated with a bleat. Jake whooped and hollered in delight, taunting the creature and mocking it, oblivious to the real reason the Titanothere had taken flight which was, at that very moment, looming behind him.

A guttural snarl made Jake turn round. A Thanator, a black, six-limbed panther from hell, stood just metres away. It opened its jaws, baring lethal fangs.

"What about this one?" Jake asked Grace. "Run, don't run?"

"Run. Definitely run!" she yelled as the creature pounced.

Jake launched himself between two large trunks, forcing the beast to claw its way to the side. He just had time to scramble over a tangle of roots before the beast extricated itself and leapt towards him. He dived under a mass of roots to take cover. Claws and jaws slashed at him. Groping for his gun Jake fired at the Thanator but although it roared with pain, it kept coming.

It gripped Jake by the backpack, lifted him clear off the ground and shook him left and right.

Jake grappled desperately with the fastening of his backpack and managed to click it open. The straps gave and he dropped to the ground, running for his life with the beast snapping at his heels.

He pushed desperately through the undergrowth and seeing water ahead, dived outward with all his might. Jake flew off the edge of a cliff, over a waterfall and down into the seething pool below.

His limbs cracked against rocks but he fought upwards and broke the surface with a gasp. As the current carried him downstream towards calmer waters he caught one last sight of the terrifying Thanator snapping at him from the edge of the cliff above.

Jake eventually managed to climb onto a bank and sat panting under a screen of giant leaves. He needed to prioritise. Having lost his gun and his crew he had to arm himself. Taking a knife from his pocket he began hacking at the end of a sapling trying to form a crude spear.

For what seemed like hours he walked through the forest, every snap of twig forcing him to take cover. Despite his hyper-alert state however, the former Marine did not notice that he was being tracked from above.

The tall, blue, beautiful hunter waited for her prey to come into full view and soundlessly rose up on the bough on which she was perched. With one, fluid movement she knocked an arrow into her bow and took aim at Jake's throat. She followed him with her bow, muscles tensed for the shot...until something drifted down in front of her.

A tiny woodsprite, like a jelly fish, floated onto the point of her arrow and balanced itself there. With a frown the girl lowered her bow and watched as below her Jake continued to track his way through the undergrowth.

As the sun set Trudy's helicopter banked over the forest. Grace and Norm scanned the ground looking for Jake. The darkness that was descending on Pandora meant that their time was up, with Trudy swinging the helicopter back towards Hell's Gate.

Grace, looking on anxiously, doubted Jake's chances of making it until morning...

Nightfall brought a fresh set of problems for Jake. All around him he caught the glint of malevolent eyes. Hastily he jammed the end of a makeshift torch into the thick sap trickling down a nearby tree trunk, then fumbled for a waterproof match from the survival kit which had mercifully remained in his pocket during the encounter with the Thanator. A few sparks flickered, but suddenly a flame appeared and the sap took light. In the light of the torch Jake finally saw his foe. A pack of gleaming black Viperwolves slunk around him, stalking him on the ground and in the trees.

Half a dozen of them loomed closer, displaying glistening black teeth set in white gums.

''I don't have all goddamn night! Come on!'' Jake screamed, whirling his torch round in an arc, desperately trying to repel the Viperwolves.

But it was no use, three of the creatures pounced. He managed to crack one of them over the head with his spear, but the others kept on coming. One grabbed his ankle and he

fell to the floor. He pulled the knife from his belt and slashed at it, wounding its shoulder. The Viperwolf pulled back but the third leapt onto his chest. Jake tried to hold it at bay, its teeth snapping inches from his throat.

Thwack!

An arrow hit the beast square in the chest. Jake rolled out from under the dead wolf just in time to see a blue amazon emerge from the trees, firing arrow after arrow into the pack. With amazing agility she whirled and jumped, cracking several Viperwolves with her bow and jabbing at others, incisors bared, until sensing defeat, they ran.

The blue girl turned to Jake, grabbed his torch and hurled it into a stream.

Jake looked on in disbelief as the flame vanished with a hiss and the forest was plunged into darkness.

>

The girl bent over the dying Viperwolf.

"Forgive me, my brother," she said softly in Na'vi, ending its torment with one clean stroke of her knife.

Jake scrambled into the creek to recover his lost spear, then straightened up. He looked around him in amazement. He could still see. The jungle was alive with bioluminescence; a galaxy of blue-green light patterned every leaf, root and branch. The effect was stunning. Jake tried to communicate with the girl, to thank her, but she ignored him and continued her Na'vi prayer ritual over the Viperwolf's corpse. As Jake stammered his gratitude, she pulled the arrow from the Viperwolf's heart and walked away.

"Hey slow down. Wait up! I just wanted to say thanks for killing those things..."

A wallop from the girl's bow laid Jake out flat before he could finish. She stood over him, shaking with rage.

"You don't thank for this! This is sad. Very sad, only," she said. "All this is your fault! They did not need to die."

"They attacked me!" Jake barked indignantly.

With one step the girl was upon him, her knife at his throat. "Your fault!" she hissed. "You're like a baby, making noise, don't know what to do."

Jake backed away. "Fine, if you love your little forest friends, why not let them just kill my ass?"

Her golden eyes met his. "You have a strong heart. No fear," she said. "But stupid! Ignorant like a child." And with that she padded away.

Jake ran after the girl who was walking fast through the forest, leaping with ease over roots and onto branches. He urged her to teach him, to change his child-like ways.

"Sky people can not learn," she replied. "You do not See."

He tried another tack, asking her where she had learned English, trying to build common ground through the link to Dr. Augustine.

He continued his dialogue as they ran over the root of an enormous tree, elevated metres from the ground, but at that moment he caught his spear in a vine and span off balance.

"Like a baby!" hissed the girl, grabbing his bicep and pulling him upright.

Jake pleaded with her to take him with her, but she would not listen.

"Go back!" she ordered, turning to face him and blocking his path.

Then, sensing a presence she looked up to see more woodsprites, pulsing with purpose, floating down towards Jake. As she watched they began dancing gently around his head and shoulders.

He swatted one away nervously, but she grabbed his arm forcefully and scolded him in Na'vi.

"*Atokirina*'!"

Jake held still and waited. He spread his arms wide and more sprites came, landing all over his arms, hands and body, until he was covered in the glowing, pulsing things. They both watched, mesmerised.

"What are they?" Jake asked.

"Seeds of the sacred tree, very pure spirits," she told him. Then just as suddenly as they'd appeared, the seeds scattered. Then, grabbing his arm, she ordered him to follow her, running off up the root. It seemed these strange seeds had brought about a change of heart.

>

They ran for miles through the jungle. Jake noticed for the first time that on the forest floor rings of light, like ripples on a pond, expanded out with each footfall. Strange foliage glowed dimly all around, but when he touched anything the light glowed brighter. He had just tried to re-initiate a conversation when there was a loud *whoosh* and a weighted rope span at him and tangled round his legs. With a yell he toppled off the root and crashed to the ground below.

Looking up he saw several Na'vi riders thundering toward him on six-legged, armour-skinned direhorses. He untangled himself and stood up, unsheathing his knife and turning in time to see more warriors pointing their arrows straight at him. Luckily for Jake his companion wasn't far behind.

As she jumped down into the fray, she demanded calm from the warriors.

She turned to the head rider Tsu'tey, a young, powerfully built warrior with sculpted features and a proud jaw line and asked him what he was doing.

Tsu'tey jumped from his mount, smoothly detaching the end of his long neural queue from the antenna of the horse.

"These demons are forbidden here Neytiri," Tsu'tey replied, indicating Jake, who had no idea what the Na'vi were saying to each other. In fact, the girl - Neytiri- was saving his hide.

"There has been a sign. This is a matter for the Tsahik!" Neytiri shouted.

Tsu'tey ordered his men to escort Jake to the Tsahik. Before Jake could react he was surrounded by warriors who grabbed his arms and began shoving him along the trail. Jake, oblivious to what was happening, cried out to his companion. But she was off ahead.

The warriors hauled Jake through the forest and at last thundered through the gap between the roots of the most enormous tree Jake had ever seen. 'Hometree' as the Na'vi called it, was so tall its top was sheathed in cloud. Its base was formed of massive mangrove-pillars. Shoved roughly into the centre of the tree his eyes widened in amazement. The clearing was lit by huge cook-fires around which squatted the Na'vi. As they passed some tried to touch him, others shied away. All gawked at the alien, expressions ranging from curiosity to outright hostility.

In the centre of the clearing the skull of an enormous creature was mounted on a totem pole. Beneath it stood an impressive Na'vi, wearing a collar of feathers and a chest mantle of Thanator claws. It was the clan leader, Eytukan. His always stern features were clouded with anger.

"Father, I See you," said Neytiri, bowing to her father and touching her forehead with her bow.

But her father wasn't best pleased, demanding to know why she had brought such a 'creature' to him.

Neytiri explained that she was about to kill him, only to be stopped by a sign from Eywa.

"I have said no dreamwalker will come here," sneered Eytukan. "His alien smell fills my nose."

Jake turned to his companion to ask what was happening.

"My father is deciding whether to kill you," she snapped.

Jake decided to adopt some normal 'meet the parents' etiquette. "Nice to meet you, Sir," he said, stepping forward and holding out a hand to Eytukan.

Wrong move. Within seconds he was shoved back, Tsu-tey's knife at his throat.

>

A commanding female voice echoed through the chamber and everyone looked up. Mo'at stood on the second level of the tree, her haughty face regarding the scene below.

"I will look at this alien," she ordered, descending the natural spiral staircase at the core of Hometree.

"This is Mother. She is Tsahik - the one who interprets the will of Eywa," explained Neytiri.

Jake, unsure of who or what 'Eywa' was, looked confused. Mo'at asked his name, taking a long thorn from her necklace, striking his chest as he told her. The blow drew blood, Mo'at ran the bloody thorn across her tongue and swallowed. She seemed dismissive when Jake insisted that he had come to learn.

"We have tried to teach other Sky People. It is hard to fill a cup which is already full," she said.

"My cup is empty, trust me. Just ask Doctor Augustine," Jake grinned, finding some humour in the situation. "I'm no scientist. I was a Marine. A warrior of the, erm... Jarhead clan." His response seemed to satisfy both Mo'at and Eytukan.

"This is the first warrior dreamwalker we have seen. We need to learn more about him," ordered Eytukan.

Mo'at nodded, telling her daughter she must teach Jake the ways of the Na'vi.

Even on Pandora parental orders jarred sometimes; "That's not fair!" bristled the girl, glaring at Jake. But it was decided.

"Learn well Jakesully," said Mo'at. "Then we will see if your insanity can be cured."

That night, Jake began life with the clan. As the girl led him up the spiral spokes inside the tree, he adjusted the thong keeping his new loincloth in place. It felt weird and uncomfortable. The entire clan were assembled for dinner. As Jake made his way round the circle to take his place round the fire he accidentally trod on someone's tail. His greetings of 'how are you?' were met with blank stares. Eventually he settled in however, eating his meal from a large leaf.

After dinner Neytiri took him up to the next level which served as the clan's sleeping quarters. Hammocks the size of trampolines were suspended from branches. Neytiri jumped in hers and Jake swung down into the next hammock.

They lay facing each other, the tension between them crackling in the air. Jake opened his mouth to speak but the girl reached over and folded the edge of her hammock over herself like a cocoon. It was time to sleep. Jake closed his eyes...

"Jake, Jake!" voices woke him from his slumber. Someone was shining a bright light in his eyes. He blinked several times. He was back in his own body with Grace, Norm and Max, who'd last seen him being hunted by the Thanator, desperately attempting to rouse him.

Eventually he roused, much to the relief of the team surrounding him. Reality crashed in as Jake realised he was back in Hell's Gate.

"Is the avatar safe?" Grace asked, anxiously regarding Jake's sweating face.

"Yeah Doc!" he answered with a grin. "And you are not gonna believe where I am!"

The story continues on Page 42

AVATAR QUIZ:
PHASE ONE

Could you survive on Pandora? Take phase one of our three part quiz to see if you've got what it takes to stay alive in this challenging environment. Answers are on Page 108.

1. The air on Pandora is toxic to humans?

True ☐
False ☐

2. Without an exo-pack and mask a human can survive for 10 minutes?

True ☐
False ☐

3. The most fearsome land predator on Pandora is the Hammerhead Titanothere?

True ☐
False ☐

4. The Direhorse is a herbivore?

True ☐
False ☐

5. The most respectful greeting one Na'vi individual can give another is 'I See you'?

True ☐
False ☐

6. The Na'vi's favoured weapon is the spear?

True ☐
False ☐

7. *Eywa* is the Na'vi deity?

True ☐
False ☐

8. The *Tsa'hik* in a Na'vi tribe is the male clan leader?

True ☐
False ☐

9. The largest flying predator on Pandora is the Forest Banshee?

True ☐
False ☐

10. The most direct way for the Na'vi to communicate with *Eywa* is through the Tree of Souls?

True ☐
False ☐

11. The Hallelujah Mountains are unique because they are semi-submerged in a huge lake?

True ☐
False ☐

12. The Hexapede provides a good source of meat for the Na'vi?

True ☐
False ☐

RDA SCIENCE:
LOCATIONS

RDA THE BIO LAB

The Bio Lab is the nerve centre of RDA Science operations and the hub of the Avatar Program. A state of the art facility, it boasts every type of bio-technology. The equipment allows the science team to dissect, study and record geological and biological samples taken during field trips on the planet. They also create video logs documenting their experiences. It is in the Bio-Lab where Avatars, arriving from earth, are stored and monitored until they are ready to be put into operation.

RDA AMNIO-TANK

The Bio-lab is equipped to house several of these huge acrylic tanks. Avatars are created in-vitro in Earth-based genetics labs and are grown en-route to Pandora in Amnio-Tanks while their operators sleep in cryo-hibernation. The five-year journey means that by the time the Avatar reach the Bio-Lab they have already reached near-adult proportions (typically 9 feet in length). The Amnio-Tank creates a womb-like environment for the Avatar. It is filled with synthetic amniotic fluid to support and cushion the life-form.

RDA WOMB-LIKE CONDITIONS

Gentle blue light mimics the effect of natural Pandoran daylight, aiding the formation of the Avatar's skin, while engineered hormones stimulate rapid growth and ensure correct organ development and muscle tone. A nutrient-rich broth circulates into the Avatar through an artificial placenta, a purpose-designed matrix of spongiform blood vessels and monitoring electrodes.

RDA THE LINK ROOM

The link room, set within the Bio-Lab, is responsible for transferring the Avatar driver's mind into the Avatar body. It contains multiple link units, placed in a circle around a central monitoring station.

RDA LINK UNIT

This is a coffin-like box about 2.5m in length. It contains a bed framed by fluid gel packs which mould into the shape of the human placed upon them. An upper clamshell fits over the body underneath the lid while the unit is in operation.

The link unit is used to connect an Avatar driver to his or her Avatar. It creates a psionic link which temporarily transfers the consciousness from a human body into an Avatar, giving the driver control over all its muscles and senses. Once the link is established, the driver can use the artificial body as if it was his own.

There is also a mobile link station containing further link units, at Site 26, in the Hallelujah Mountains.

RDA TRANSFER CHAMBER

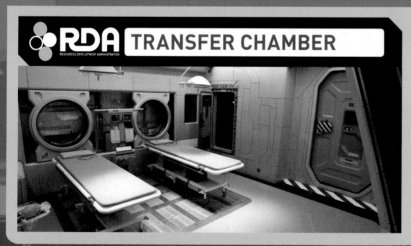

This is an unpressurized room directly connected to the Link Room, where Avatars are decanted from the Amnio-Tank. After decant, the artificial placenta and umbilical cord are removed.

Technicians scan and check the Avatar for defects and implant bio-electrically powered electrodes and processor circuits necessary for the control link interface. The room has the capability to bring two Avatars out of their tanks simultaneously.

RDA AVATAR COMPOUND

This is the external area where new Avatar Drivers can acclimatise to Pandoran conditions. It serves as a useful stepping stone between the Earth-like environment within Hell's Gate and the dangerous Pandoran jungle beyond the razor fence. The compound contains a military-style obstacle course and gym for fitness training, a basketball court for recreation and a kitchen and the longhouse - a dormitory where the Avatars can be placed for rest when not in use.

RDA SCIENCE:
CLOTHING & ACCESSORIES

RDA t-shirts, vests or short sleeved shirts

The science team wear civilian clothing when on-base in human form. When in Avatar form, they wear bespoke items designed to allow them to move easily through jungle terrain.
This includes:

RDA combat trousers or shorts

RDA sturdy walking boots

RDA socks

CIVILIAN EXOPACK

Consisting of a mask and portable base unit, this lightweight atmosphere filtration system allows humans to survive on Pandora with a minimum amount of equipment. The exopack utitilizes a full-face, transparent, sealed faceplate which is connected by a hose to a small pack containing the filters and power supply.

WEAPONS & EQUIPMENT ↵

RDA · CARB Assault Rifle (Civilian)

Usage: General security for non-military, this is also standard issue for non Sec-Ops personnel working outside the wire.

RDA · Machete

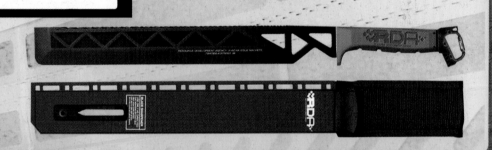

Usage: Favoured by Grace, this is a useful kit for collecting botanic samples.

RDA · Avatar Issue Pouch

Usage: Stored on utility belt and used to store small equipment and essentials.

RDA · Communications Handset

Usage: Used to communicate when separated or in different locations.

RDA · Knife

Usage: General issue equipment for all Avatars.

MEETING NEYTIRI AND SPENDING THE EVENING WITH THE CLAN HAD BEEN THE MOST AMAZING EXPERIENCE OF JAKE'S LIFE, BUT NOW IT WAS BACK TO REAL LIFE. OVER BREAKFAST, THE SCIENTISTS CRANED FORWARD TO HEAR ABOUT JAKE'S EXPLOITS.

"The last thing we see is this Marine's ass disappearing into the brush with an angry Thanator coming after him," said Grace.

Jake beamed as he took the group's praise, the other avatar drivers clapped him on the back.

"For some reason I can't fathom, the Omaticaya have chosen you," Grace smiled. "God help us all."

Only one driver didn't look pleased at Jake's success. Norm stared sombrely into his bowl, silently fuming at the injustice of a total novice being welcomed into the clan.

When Jake reported to Quaritch and Selfridge for a debriefing, they were highly amused by his excursion.

The fact that he had used the Jarhead clan was of particular amusement.

But his exploits in infiltrating the Na'vi weren't overlooked, with Selfridge particularly impressed.

"That's called taking the initiative, son. I wish I had ten more like you."

The conversation then took a sinister turn. Selfridge demanded that Jake discover a way to get the Na'vi, or the "blue monkeys" in his words, to move.

Previous offers of medicine, education and roads had fallen short. He zoomed a 3D graphic map of Pandora into Hometree.

"Their damn village is resting on the richest Unobtanium deposit within two hundred klicks in any direction."

Jake's mission was crystal clear – he had to persuade the clan to relocate. He shook his head, shaken by the enormity of this task.

"Killing the indigenous looks bad, but if there's one thing shareholders hate more than bad press, it's a bad quarterly statement," said Selfridge. "So just find me a carrot that will get them to move...otherwise..." he glanced at the Colonel, "...it's going to have to be all stick, OK?"

"You got three months," Quaritch warned. "That's when the bulldozers get there."

Grace was determined to cram as much information about the Omaticaya clan into Jake's head as possible before he returned to his avatar body. She flashed image after image of clan members in front of him, testing his scant knowledge of the tribe.

"Mo'at. Dragon Lady," said Jake, then... "Eytukan."

Grace corrected his pronunciation. "He's the clan leader, but she's the spiritual leader. Like a shaman," she told him.

"Tsu'tey," Jake continued, as the image of the fearsome warrior he'd encountered flashed before him.

"He will be the next clan leader," Grace nodded.

"Neytiri," Jake said, his voice softer as he gazed fondly at the girl who had saved him from the Viperwolves the day before.

"She will be the next *Tsahik*. She and Tsu'tey will become a mated pair," Grace said.

"So who's this Eywa?" Jake asked, climbing into the link.

Norm was incredulous. "Only their deity. Their Goddess. Made up of all living things. You'd know this if you had any training whatsoever."

Grace flicked some switches on Jake's link, preparing him for his passage back to Pandora.

She warned him not to do anything "unusually stupid" as he closed his eyes and returned to his avatar form.

>

Back with the Omaticaya, Jake had much to learn. Neytiri took him out to a meadow near a river where a herd of six-legged Direhorses, with armoured skin and long antennae, were grazing on the nectar of flowers. It was time to learn to ride like a Na'vi warrior.

Neytiri held the Direhorse's leads while Jake clumsily mounted. He gripped one of the Direhorse's antenna with one hand and the neural queue at the end of his hair in the other. Slowly he brought the two together. The Direhorse's intakes flared and its eyes widened as the tendrils interwove.

"That is 'Shahaylu', the bond," Neytiri said. "Feel her heartbeat, her breath. Feel her strong legs."

Jake closed his eyes, nodding. One with the Direhorse.

"You may tell her what to do," Neytiri touched her head, "...inside. For now, say where to go."

On Jake's command the Direhorse launched forward into a gallop, with no idea how to sit the animal, Jake was flung unceremoniously into the mud. Neytiri roared with laughter as she jogged after the Direhorse.

Jake looked up just in time to see Tsu'tey and another hunter thunder up on their Direhorses. Jake wiped mud from his face as Tsu'tey brought his Direhorse to a stand, looking down at him with disdain. Tsu'tey told Jake he should leave, complaining to Neytiri: "This alien will learn nothing. A rock Sees more," he said in Na'vi. Neytiri just smiled and turned to Jake, gesturing to the Direhorse and ordering him to try again.

Jake's days were filled learning the ways of the Omaticayan people. When night fell and his avatar slept, he returned to his human body where he swotted more facts with the science team or visited the military team for a debriefing.

After several weeks he had enough information about the structure of Hometree to pass on.

"This is the view from the East," he told the Colonel and Selfridge, showing them the tree on the graphic display. "If you go in the main entrance there's an outer row of columns, real heavy duty. There's a secondary ring here, and an inner ring. There's a core structure, like a spiral, that's how they move up and down."

"We're going to need accurate scans on every column," Quaritch told his engineers.

Jake, Quaritch and Selfridge were so wrapped up in their discussion, that no-one clocked Max, hovering outside the door, listening with horror.

When Jake reported back to the Bio-lab it was to find Grace, Norm and Max hastily slinging equipment into bags and cases.

"So where are we going?" Jake asked.

Grace, having been updated by Max, was moving the operation to a mobile link up at Site 26, somewhere they could work in the mountains.

"Yesss!" laughed Norm looking happy for the first time in weeks. "The legendary Floating Mountains of Pandora!" He shot Jake a look. "Heard of them?"

Though there was obvious hostility towards Jake, they knew he was their only chance of securing a peaceful resolution.

>

The group set off in Trudy's helicopter, climbing high into the mist-shrouded mountains. As they flew through enormous arches of rock, Grace warned the group that they were getting closer. It was confirmed by Trudy's instruments. Flying into the flux vortex made the displays and dials on the dash go crazy. Not only that, such was the visibility - or lack of - that Trudy couldn't even see where she was going. Though Norm panicked, Trudy seemed to relish the challenge of flying blind.

A cloud bank parted revealing the Hallelujah Mountains in all their glory. Jake and Norm gaped at the archipelago of huge islands hovering among the clouds. Clusters of vines hung beneath them and waterfalls streamed down the sides, evaporating below.

"Oh my God!" breathed Norm.

"You should see your faces," giggled Trudy.

The remote research station consisted of two bus-shaped airlift modules and was very basic. Four bunks and a fridge sat among a clutter of equipment.

"Welcome to camp," Grace said, leading them inside. She began flicking lights and equipment on. Trudy helped herself to food while Jake checked out photographs taped to the fridge's door showing Grace posing at her school with various Na'vi children including a younger Neytiri. Staring at the smiling faces of Grace with the Omaticaya he understood why Grace had allowed him to come, despite knowing he was reporting to Colonel. He represented a way back in with the clan.

"Jake, hang a left," Grace instructed, showing him into a side room containing several link units. "You'll be in the link at the end. Beulah, she's the least glitchy."

Settling himself in to the unit's gel bed Jake closed his eyes, eager to get back to Neytiri.

Neytiri had yet more surprises and challenges in store for Jake. That day she took him to the very top of Hometree. She leapt up the core trunk while he did his best to keep up. When he thought he couldn't climb one more step she led him outside onto a branch. Through gaps in the foliage Jake could see other Great Trees scattered across the landscape, like enormous umbrellas, 325 metres above the ground.

Neytiri took a few strides and began making a series of clicks and calls. In the branches above, dark shapes stirred, rustling the leaves. Suddenly, a huge Mountain Banshee with a 12 metre wingspan swooped down toward them, alighting on the branch in front of Neytiri.

Jake stumbled backwards as the enormous dragon-like creature flapped its huge wings with a deafening crack.

"Don't look her in her eye," Neytiri warned. Jake did as he was told, averting his gaze as she fed the banshee a morsel of meat, murmuring to it and stroking its neck.

She then caught hold of her hair and gently connected it to the banshee's antenna. The creature shivered and stretched its wings as the neural connection was made.

"Once *Tsahaylu* is made. *Ikran* will fly with only one hunter in the whole life," she said climbing smoothly onto the animal's back and settling into the harness. "To become *taronyu* 'hunter' you must choose your own *Ikran*. And he must choose you.

"When?" asked Jake, excited by the prospect.

"When you are ready" answered Neytiri, lowering her flight visor and urging the banshee into flight. She flew it in circles around the tree, swooping and diving, in perfect fusion with her winged mount. Jake watched in awe.

\>

Jakes days began to blur together. There were language sessions and lessons in hunting and tracking. As physically challenging as the environment was, he found the language the most difficult. But he coped by approaching it as he would have approached field-stripping a weapon in his Marine days.

Neytiri crouched before him, saying the words and had him repeat them over and over again. When he failed she called him *Skxawng*, Na'vi for moron. Despite being used to more advanced weaponry, he loved the feel of the longbow. Neytiri showed him how to stand tall and use his core muscles to create the perfect arc for the shot. She taught him that a network of energy flows through all living things. She said that all energy is only borrowed and one day it must be given back.

Whenever the avatar slept, Jake returned to his body for more coaching with Grace. Even Norm, who initially struggled to accept Jake's role, was now helpful. It was Norm who taught Jake the meaning of the Na'vi greeting 'I see you'.

"It's not just 'I'm seeing you in front of me, it's I see into you, '*I See you*'," Norm explained.

As Jake's schooling in the ways of the Na'vi continued, he began to make progress. His feet got tougher and he could run faster and farther every day. He learnt to trust his body to know what to do - a vital skill since with Neytiri it was a case of learn fast or die.

More importantly, he sweet-talked Mo'at into allowing Grace back into the village for the first time since the school had been closed. It warmed his heart to see her reunited with her former pupils.

One evening Jake had a breakthrough - his first clean kill. As he pulled his arrow from the twitching body of the deer-like Hexapede, he leant over it and said in halting Na'vi.

"I See you Brother, and thank you. Your spirit goes with Eywa, your body stays behind to become part of the People."

Neytiri looked on approvingly. He was ready.

That day they rode the Direhorses up the trail to a beanstalk-like formation. Boulders of Unobtanium hung suspended in thick vine-like trees.

"Now what?" Jake asked realising that the trail was becoming too steep for the Direhorses.

Neytiri turned back but beckoned for him to follow the others - Tsu'tey and two young hunters ready to pass the test and learn to ride an *Ikran*.

The hunters leapt nimbly along the vine trunks, climbing toward the floating islands above. Eventually they reached Mons Veritatis, one of the biggest mountains on Pandora.

Jake stared over the sheer cliff face. He felt dizzy. Just then there was a shriek and Neytiri, majestic on her banshee, swooped in to perch on the edge of the grotto. She smiled at Jake and turned to Tsu'tey who saluted her.

Tsu'tey smirked as he told Jake that he would be the first up. Jake headed out to a perilous ledge and tiptoed along. It opened onto a banshee rookery. Hundreds of banshees huddled on the rocky outcrop, clinging to the walls with their fore-claws or perching on ledges.

"Now you choose your *Ikran*," whispered Neytiri. "This you must feel inside. If he also chooses you, move quick, like I showed. You will have one chance, Jake."

"How will I know if he chooses me?" Jake said.

"He will try to kill you," came the answer.

Jake eased forward. 'Outstanding!' he thought, unfurling his weighted leather strap.

>

The banshees eyed him suspiciously. Several shrieked and took flight as he approached. Others showed rows of fangs in a threat display.

One, a huge male, turned towards him. Jake opened his mouth and hissed at the beast which shrieked back at him.

"Let's dance!" Jake exclaimed, swinging his line. But catching an *Ikran* was no simple feat. As Jake lunged, the banshee almost caught him with its claws. He sidestepped away just in time, managing to swing his line around the beast's jaws, clamping them shut.

With a huge leap he was on the banshee's back, but the beast bucked and lurched like a rodeo bull. Tsu'tey laughed, watching Jake cling on - gloating that Jake was about to die.

With an angry shriek the banshee tossed Jake off. He flew over the edge of the precipice, grasping at vines to stop himself from plummeting to his death.

Even Neytiri seemed convinced of his failure. "Jake!" she screamed.

Using all his strength Jake pulled himself back onto the ledge and leapt onto the banshee, hauling it to the ground. Now beast and man lay eye to eye.

"*Tsahaylu* - make the bond!" urged Neytiri.

With one deft movement Jake brought the end of his hair into the banshee's antenna. The struggle was over - Jake and the beast were one.

"That's right, you're mine," Jake told his banshee, relaxing his grip and allowing the beast upright. Neytiri ran to him proudly.

"First flight seals the bond. You cannot wait," she told him. "Think 'fly'!"

Jake repeated the instruction and the banshee, now programmed to obey even the most hesitant command from its hunter, swooped into the air.

It took Jake some time to master the beast. At first it hurtled downwards in a death spin so violent Jake was almost shaken off. They hit a wall and the banshee's cries were so loud he was unable to think.

"Shut up! And fly straight!" he cried out in desperation. Hearing his intent the banshee did just that and from then on followed Jake's thoughts.

"Bank left," he told it. Then, "level out." At each command the beast complied. Jake felt like he was born to do this.

Watching from above the young hunters whooped their approval and congratulations until Tsu'tey silenced them. Neytiri, however, wanted to share Jake's success with him. With a bound she was on her banshee, swooping down to fly in tandem.

Over the next few days they did little else but fly and hunt. Jake was in heaven as they explored corners of Pandora he had never seen before. They even flew to 'Vitraya Ramunong'

the tree of souls, a gnarled and ancient willow tree nestling amongst arches of magnetic rock.

Grace, knowing that it was the Na'vi's most sacred place and that outsiders were strictly forbidden, couldn't believe it when Jake admitted he'd seen it.

Then one day, just as Jake was beginning to feel invincible, he had a new encounter. He was flying with Neytiri along a forested ridge when a shadow fell over them.

A huge crested predator, several times larger than the banshee, striped scarlet, yellow and black, bore down on them from above. The hunters had become the hunted.

It took all of Jake's aerial acrobatic skills to lead himself and Neytiri through the forest. The predator snapped and lurched at them, almost catching them between its jaws, but when all seemed lost, Jake managed to steer them into undergrowth too thick for the predator to follow.

>

Back at Hometree, a shaken Jake fingered the fangs of the skull attached to the totem with renewed respect. It was the skeletal remains of the same type of predator which had almost caught them.

Known to his scientist friends as a Great Leonopteryx, Neytiri revealed the Na'vi name for the best - *Toruk*, Last Shadow.

"The last one you ever see," Jake nodded.

Jumping up to join Jake on the platform, Neytiri explained the legend of *Toruk Makto* - Rider of Last Shadow. There had been only five since time began and her grandfather's grandfather was one.

"*Toruk* chose him," Neytiri explained. "*Toruk Makto* is mighty. He brought the clans together in a time of great sorrow. All Na'vi people know this story."

As Jake returned to his real body that night, he pondered the events of the past three months. He'd become so immersed in the Na'vi culture, he could barely remember his old life nor make out which was the true world and which was the dream. Everything seemed backwards... and now it was time to report back to Quaritch.

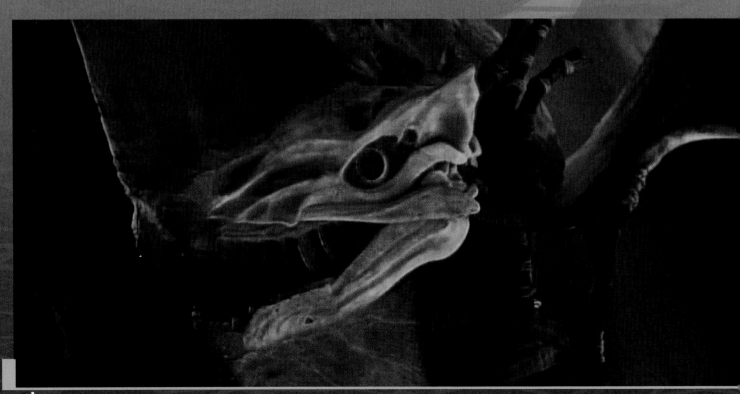

The Colonel was waiting for Jake in the commissary. He did not look happy.

Quaritch was doubting Jake's resolve, accusing him of getting "lost in the woods". Jake's last video report was more than two weeks ago.

"It's time to terminate the mission."

Jake's eyes flared with alarm.

"No!" he cried. "I can do this!"

"You already have. You gave me good usable intel and now it's time to come in."

Jake felt hollow inside as the Colonel explained he'd done the deal for Jake to have the surgery to give him back his legs. Jake thought fast.

"I've gotta finish this. There's one more thing - a ceremony, the final stage of becoming a man. If I do it I'm one of them. And they'll trust me..." he paused, hardly able to finish his sentence. "and I can negotiate the terms of their relocation."

"Well then you'd better get it done, Corporal." Quaritch glared, striding out of the room.

>

As Neytiri painted Jake's face and body that night, daubing it with stripes befitting an Omaticayan warrior, she had no idea of his troubled thoughts. He sat still and let her finish her work, but his mind was elsewhere.

Then together they descended into the enclosure at the centre of Hometree where the entire clan had gathered. Eytukan placed both hands on Jake's chest and held them there.

"You are now a son of the Omaticaya. You are part of the People," he declared solemnly. As Grace watched, her eyes brimming with tears, several other members of the clan pressed forward, crowding around and putting their hands on Jake's shoulders, back and chest. Other members put their hands on the shoulders of those clan members until Jake was at the centre of a huge web of people. Belonging. Connected.

When the ceremony ended, Neytiri took Jake to an exquisitely beautiful glade of willows. The pair stood amid the tendrils.

"This is a place for prayers to be heard. And sometimes answered," she told Jake, taking the end of her hair and placing it on the tendrils.

She took a deep breath and Jake saw the tendrils wrap round the willow frond.

"We call these trees *Utray Mokri* - the Tree of Voices. The voices of our ancestors - they live within Eywa."

Jake took his hair and did the same, then blinked hard as he heard the whispering of ancient Na'vi voices.

As they stood listening, several woodsprite circled them, some alighting on their shoulders and arms. They were very close now. She looked at him and he felt drawn into her gaze.

"You are Omaticaya now," she said touching his chest. "You may make your own bow from the wood of Hometree and you may choose a woman..."

She tried to sound casual and turned away as she extolled the virtues of other female tribe members.

"Ninat is the best singer.
Beyral is a good hunter..."

Jake smiled and nodded. "I've
already chosen," he told her, his gaze
intense. "But this woman must also
choose me."

"She already has," Neytiri
answered.

Kissing and using their hair
tendrils to forge the unbreakable
bond of a mated pair, they came
together. Finally, they fell asleep
together on the bed of moss. As his
avatar lost consciousness, Jake
returned to his body in the link.

>

At dawn Jake couldn't wait to get back to Neytiri, but Grace was worried about his shattered appearance. Before he could rush back to Pandora, she prepared him breakfast.

In the clearing a crunching noise woke Neytiri. She blinked beside Jake's unconscious avatar body. Something was coming...something big. A crashing sound brought her to her feet. A huge machine was rolling through the jungle, tearing up the trees and bearing down on the willows under which they lay.

"Jake! Wake up! Please!" she cried. She shook him violently, but he remained unconscious.

Stuck in his real body Jake shovelled food down as fast as he could. He began climbing into the link before he'd had time to swallow.

"All done, let's go!" he told Grace, lying down on the gel bed.

"Jesus, Marine, when was the last time you took a shower!" Grace exclaimed, finally shutting the lid.

Jake re-inhabited his avatar body just in time. Neytiri was frantically dragging him out of the path of a line of bulldozers that were crashing through the undergrowth.

"Stop!" he yelled, jumping up and waving his arms. When they continued on their destructive path he leapt onto one of them and began smashing in the camera lenses with a rock. A trooper in an AMP Suit fired at him. Jake leapt off to avoid being hit.

Tears poured down Neytiri's cheeks and Jake's features hardened in anger. Together they watched helplessly as the Na'vi's sacred site was destroyed.

Back at the Ops Centre the Colonel was watching footage from the scene. He glared at a monitor showing an angry native smashing the camera before the screen went blank. He hit rewind and froze the picture on a close-up of the native's face. Jake's angry avatar features filled the screen. Seconds later Quaritch was on a helicopter bound for the mountains.

Meanwhile at Hometree, the Omaticaya were making a plan. Eytukan ordered that Tsu'tey would lead the war party - the people were incensed, and wanted revenge.

Grace tried to talk them out of it, insisting that it'd only make things worse, but Tsu'tey was unrepentant.

"We will strike them in the heart!" he cried, raising his bow. At that moment Jake and Neytiri strode in. Jake pleaded with Tsu'tey to stop and think but the warrior was incensed as Neytiri admitted to the group that she and Jake were mated before Eywa.

"I have something to say!" Jake cried in Na'vi, parrying the blow. "I am one of you and I have the right to speak! I have something to say to all of you," he paused. "The words are like stones in my heart."

Jake looked into the expectant faces of Eytukan, Mo'at and his beloved Neytiri, then without warning he collapsed.

Beside him Grace also fell to the ground. The Colonel had arrived at the remote outpost, overpowered Norm and pulled the plug on the link units.

The story continues on Page 66

AVATAR QUIZ:
PHASE TWO

Are you familiar with RDA's operations on Pandora? Take the second phase of this three part test to find out. Answers are on Page 108.

1. RDA stands for...

A: Reconnaissance and Development Association.
B: Research and Distribution Agency.
C: Resources and Development Administration.

2. The journey from Earth to Pandora takes approximately...

A: Five years.
B: Four months.
C: Three years.

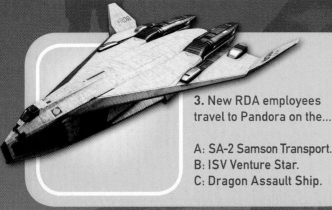

3. New RDA employees travel to Pandora on the...

A: SA-2 Samson Transport.
B: ISV Venture Star.
C: Dragon Assault Ship.

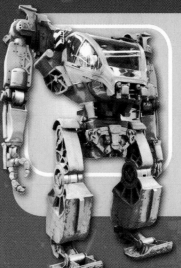

4. An AMP Suit allows a Sec-Ops trooper to...

A: Perform amplified versions of any human activity.
B: Outrun any creature on Pandora.
C: Avoid the effects of the Flux Vortex.

5. An Avatar within the RDA Avatar Program is...

A: A virtual version of an individual.

B: The result of the process of mixing human and Na'vi DNA which scientists then link with a human 'consciousness'.

C: The result of a dream a driver has when asleep in a link unit.

6. Briefing talks for Sec-OPS staff would normally take place in the...

A: Operations Centre.

B: Armour Bay.

C: Commissary.

7. Unobtainium is worth...

A: $2 million a kilo in its unrefined state.

B: $20 million a kilo in its unrefined state.

C: $2 billion a kilo in its unrefined state.

8. The person in charge of all operations on Pandora is...

A: Grace Augustine.

B: Parker Selfridge.

C: Miles Quaritch.

9. Jake Sully was primarily chosen as an Avatar driver because...

A: He shares his deceased twin brother's DNA.

B: Of his military background and training.

C: Officials knew he needed the cash for an operation to repair his spinal cord.

10. The more popular name for RDA Extra Solar Colony 01 is...

A: Hell's Kitchen.

B: Hell's Teeth.

C: Hell's Gate.

10. A human Avatar driver cannot inhabit his Na'vi Avatar form without...

A: An operational link-unit

B: Being dropped into a tribe like the Omaticaya

C: An exo-pack

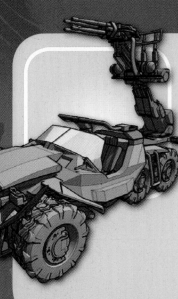

11. Why are troopers less keen to pilot The Swan Ground Assault Vehicle?

A: Because it moves slowly and in a cumbersome fashion like a Swan.

B: Because the gunner rides on an unprotected, raised platform like a sitting duck.

C: Because it is the Na'vi's most feared and hated vehicle and thus more likely to be attacked.

RDA MILITARY LOCATIONS:
HELL'S GATE

Welcome to Resource Development Administration 01, also known as Hell's Gate. Within the wire new RDA recruits. Outside the wire it's

Hell's Gate is the main centre for all human colonial activities on Pandora, and contains the planet's only spaceport. It is in a constant state of siege from both the toxic environment and Pandoran wildlife; hence the pentagonal perimeter fence which is made of razor wire and the major weapon towers at each apex which defend against surface, air and underground intrusions. A cleared, thirty-metre-wide strip surrounds the base, which is regularly patrolled by automatic plant-clearing machinery to keep the jungle at bay.

The Operations Centre

Also known as the OPS centre, this is the nexus for RDA's communications and operational control on Pandora. It occupies the largest building in Hell's Gate's administration complex and comprises a communication center, meeting rooms, and living quarters used by the DA executive staff. It also contains the control room where supervisors monitor all mining, refining, transport and security conditions on Pandora via a continuously updated holo-table display. Flight tracking is also monitored from the control room.

The Administrator's Office

Currently occupied by Parker Selfridge, this is also situated inside the OPS Centre. It is decorated with artefacts and mementoes from Pandora. A precious lump of Unobtanium takes pride of place on Parker's desk.

The Commissary

Commonly known as Hell's Kitchen this is a recreational facility where troops meet, eat and relax. It is also used for briefing large groups.

The Airfield

This takes up two thirds of Hell's Gate and features a runway and 2 landing pads connected by a taxiway.

The Armour Bay

All vehicles and machinery are stored, repaired and refitted in this building which houses the biggest concentration of light-medium weaponry outside Earth. Due to its role as the core of Hell's Gate's defences, it is protected by metre-thick walls made of concrete and fused local rock. It is the main storage area of all AMP Suits and has a large fortified hangar for the Dragon Assault Ships and Scorpion Gunships. There is also a small weights room inside a weapons locker. The Sec-Ops barracks adjoin the Armour Bay.

The Science Wing

Contains the Bio-Lab, link room and Avatar Compound. See pages 38-39 for more details.

THE MINE

The existence of Unobtanium was the main reason for RDA to establish a human colony on Pandora.

Extremely valuable in monetary terms, the ore is mined from three simple open-cast pits.

The RDA operation is the only source for Unobtanium although it is known to exist in at least twenty-five other places on the planet.

Ore is blasted from the ground then removed by excavators and robodozers and taken by trucks for refining. The mine is thought to have a life-span of around 30-years.

Staff must not to expose themselves to high radiation levels for more than 20 minutes a day and work in specially shielded vehicles.

RDA MILITARY: CLOTHING & ACCESSORIES

Standard issue Sec-Ops clothing for troopers was modified from styles worn in Earth-based military services to better fit the strains of life on Pandora. Items include:

Short-sleeved shirt
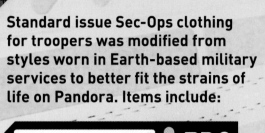
Worn inside Hell's Gate when on duty, this is often discarded during sorties outside the fence due to high temperatures.

Military Vest
Standard issue for all troopers this protective offers some protection around the torso against Na'vi arrows. Includes utility belt with pouch for knife etc.

Military Exopack
As with civilian pack, but in camouflage colour-way and with larger pack and longer power supply in case of becoming stranded outside the fence. Filters function for two weeks before accumulated soot clogs the filter pores. But filter pads can be regenerated by gentle washing with running water and last indefinitely with proper care.

RDA Dog Tag
Used for identification. Also contains access chip for specific sections on base.

Helmet

When worn with exopack, provides near total protection to head.

Communications Handset
Used to communicate when separated or in different locations

Combat trousers
Lightweight, durable, with extra storage.

Boots

Sturdy and durable.

WEAPONS

CARB Submachine Gun/Base Unit

Usage: Defensive use inside Hell's Gate and escort and patrol use beyond the wire.

Special info: Bullpup configuration (action and magazine both behind the trigger) makes it more effective at a great distance.

CARB Combat Shotgun

Usage: Force multiplier during security missions. Effective in close combat. Pellets cause horrific injuries at close-range.

Special info: Used as a backstop defensive measure, this weapon can use a wide array of twenty millimetre munitions.

Bushboss FD-3 Military Flamethrower

Usage: Clearing large, impenetrable areas of flora inside the jungle.

Special info: Portable defoliant tool used by contractors to clear brush and occasionally in battle. Its body is bulletproof and shatterproof.

MBS 9-M 50-Caliber Hydra

Usage: Door gun primarily used on Samson Transport and Gunships.

Special info: Sequential, single pulse, single barrel weapon capable of firing 600, 1200 or 1800 rounds per minute on automatic.

SN-9 Wasp Revolver

Usage: Protection against large animals and indigenous population.

Special info: Has reliability of a revolver plus extra punch to ensure enemy goes down when hit. Often acquired privately by soldiers on Pandora when standard sidearms are not sufficient.

RDA Grenades

Usage: Handheld explosives issued to RDA soldiers. Used in battle.

Special info: Boasts a delay adjustment dial. Perfectly round shape means it can be rolled as well as thrown.

RDA MILITARY: VEHICLES: AIRCRAFT

RDA **ISV VENTURE STAR**

FIELD NAME: The Dragonfly

NA'VI NAME: Wandering Star

FUNCTION: Interstellar vehicle designed to transport personnel, supplies, refined ore, equipment and data between Earth and other star systems.

SIZE: Length = 1502.4m, Width = 302.5m, Height = 218.3m.

SPEED: 167,000 miles per second at full acceleration. Takes two months to fully accelerate and to decelerate.

NOTES: One of mankind's great technological achievements and complete with built in cryo-vault, the ship is nevertheless at constant risk of catastrophic failure.

RDA **AT-99 GUNSHIP**

FIELD NAME: Scorpion

NA'VI NAME: Kunsip

FUNCTION: Aerial attack vehicle designed to eliminate threats from ground troops or aerial assault.

SIZE: Length = 11.17m, Width = 8.72m, Height = 3.51m.

SPEED: Maximum of 222 miles per hour.

NOTES: The distinctive whine of its twin tilt rotors has been known to cause stampedes of Pandoran fauna.

RDA **C-21 DRAGON ASSAULT SHIP**

FIELD NAME: Dragon, Drag Ass or Killer Diller

NA'VI NAME: Kunsip apxa

FUNCTION: Heavily defended weapons platform and troop transport for combat missions, including transport of AMP Suits, with massive array of weaponry for battle domination.

SIZE: Length = 41.5m, Width = 31.7m, Height = 9.22m.

SPEED: 105 knots in Pandoran atmosphere.

NOTES: Boasts enough non-nuclear fire-power to devastate several city blocks in seconds. Despite armour and multiple defensive guns, it remains susceptible to enemy missile strike. It is believed to be invulnerable to Na'vi weapons and animals.

 RDA **SA-2 SAMSON TRANSPORT**

FIELD NAME: Samson, Cherry-Ferry or Strong Man

NA'VI NAME: The Seed Carrier

FUNCTION: Twin-turbine VTOL rotorcraft used on Pandora for close air support and transport roles.

SIZE: Length = 15.97m, Width = 15.05m, Height = 5.25m.

SPEED: 125 knots in Pandoran atmosphere.

NOTES: Incredibly manoeuvrable due to independent rotor function and field tested for years on Earth prior to use on Pandora.

RDA **VALKYRIE SSTO-TAV-37 SHUTTLE**

FIELD NAME: Valkyrie

NA'VI NAME: Shah-tell

FUNCTION: Moves cargo, supplies and personnel between orbiting ISV and the surface of Pandora.

SIZE: Length = 80.03m, Width = 101.73m, Height = 8.0m.

SPEED: 130 knots on Pandora. 35,000 knots outside Pandoran atmosphere.

NOTES: Sudden Pandoran wind shears can cause extreme turbulence that passengers and crew liken to riding a rodeo bull. During battle for the Tree of Souls Valkyrie 16 was loaded with crates of 'daisycutter' explosives which were going to be offloaded from the cargo ramp onto the target. This effectively turned the shuttle into a bomber.

VEHICLES: GROUND VEHICLES

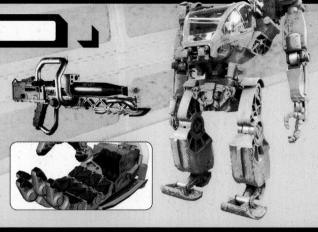

RDA — MK-6 AMPLIFIED WEAPONS PLATFORM

FIELD NAME: AMP Suit

NA'VI NAME: Shield-that-walks

FUNCTION: Multi-purpose machine able to mimic the abilities of an infantry soldier. Used on Pandora for construction, field and mining security, Hell's Gate perimeter defence and heavy combat support. Offers effective protection from toxic Pandoran environment.

SIZE: Width = 2.83m, Height = 4.205m, Weight = 1,700 kilos.

SPEED: Dependent on speed and reactions of its driver.

NOTES: Using the suit, a driver is able to punch through a tree-trunk, lift a half ton cargo crate, or rapidly build prefab units without a construction crew. The suit's weapons are, however, even more lethal than its raw strength. Incorporates huge, hip-fired GAU autocannon, optional flamethrower and long, self-sharpening combat knife.

RDA — D-22 ROB SERIES 2 REMOTELY OPERATED BULLDOZER

FIELD NAME: Robodozer or Dozer

NA'VI NAME: Unknown, but the Na'vi fear and despise this machine as one of the great evils brought by human colonists.

FUNCTION: Remotely piloted for site clearing, road building and mine operations.

SIZE: Length = 39.70m, Width = 26.93m, Height = 13.35m.

SPEED: Dependent on speed and reactions of its driver.

NOTES: The dozer is controlled remotely from the operations centre at Hell's Gate. The machine is directed through the use of a camera system. If the cameras are destroyed, the vehicle is essentially stuck.

RDA — ATV GRINDER

FIELD NAME: The Grinder

NA'VI NAME: Unkown

FUNCTION: Ground assault vehicle used for small-scale firepower support.

SIZE: Exact dimensions unknown.

SPEED: Undocumented.

NOTES: The Grinder has proved effective in hit-and-run attacks from rear against Na'vi warriors and Viperwolf packs. Although armored at the front, the sides and rear of the vehicle are extremely vulnerable to melee attacks and arrows. This problem is reinforced by its acceleration.

RDA — HEAVY-DUTY DUMP TRUCK SERIES 2

FIELD NAME: Dumper

NA'VI NAME: Unkown

FUNCTION: Transport of ore or soil

SIZE: Length = 21.12m, Width = 10.14m, Height = 6.21m.

NOTES: One of the largest land vehicles ever built and mostly manufactured on Pandora. In near-Earth gravity, roads have to be compacted to keep the unit from sinking up to its chassis.

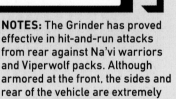

RDA — SLASH-CUTTER HEAVY-DUTY MODEL 10

FIELD NAME: Slice-and-dicer or Pizza-cutter

NA'VI NAME: Long-armed blade

FUNCTION: Brush clearance for mining operations.

SIZE: Circular blade is 2.74m in diameter.

SPEED: 130 knots on Pandora reaching 35,000 knots outside Pandoran atmosphere

NOTES: Nicknamed pizza-cutter because of blade's resemblance to circular tool for slicing pizza.

RDA — GROUND ASSAULT VEHICLE GAV JL-723

FIELD NAME: The Swan or Hellrider

NA'VI NAME: Unknown

FUNCTION: 6x6 assault vehicle, designed to travel quickly over rough landscape for combat operations.

SIZE: Length = 3.6m, Width = 1.2m.

SPEED: Unrecorded.

NOTES: The extended gunner's chair can rise above the vehicle to see over obstructions between the gun and the target, like the long neck of a swan. Troopers christened the GAV 'Hellrider' because the gunner must ride high and unprotected.

ALONE AT THE RESEARCH
STATION, NORM HAD
DONE HIS BEST TO STOP
QUARITCH SHUTTING
DOWN THE OPERATION.
"NO, NO, HOLD ON SIR,"
HE CRIED, STEPPING IN
FRONT OF THE COLONEL.
"YOU CAN'T INTERRUPT
A LINK IN PROGRESS! IT'S
DANGEROUS!"

But the Colonel was unstoppable. Shoving Norm violently against a wall, he slammed the 'off' button on both Grace and Jake's link units.

In the clearing at Hometree, the clan surveyed Grace and Jake's unconscious avatar forms, now slumped on the ground.

"You see, it is a demon in a false body. It should not live," screamed Tsu'tey, unsheathing his knife and grabbing Jake by the hair.

With an ear-piercing shriek Neytiri lunged at Tsu'tey, blind-siding the warrior and sending him sprawling to the ground. Neytiri crouched like a lioness over Jake, her knife and teeth bared, ears flattened to her head. She snarled with primal fury. Shocked at her passion, Tsu'tey backed off, panting.

Jake slammed open his link and sat up, angrily surveying the scene. Norm was backed up against a wall, looking terrified. The Colonel stood before him, his face a grim mask.

"You crossed the line," said Quaritch, punching Jake hard in the face and knocking him out. He ordered a trooper to take Jake away, and similar rough treatment was used on Grace and Norm, too. The trio were cuffed and escorted by troopers to the waiting helicopters.

Back at Hell's Gate, Jake and Grace were hauled before Selfridge.

Despite Grace's insistence that there was time to salvage the mission, Quaritch was in no mood for discussions.

Grace turned to Selfridge, hoping for a more sympathetic ear, and explained the importance of the trees that his men had destroyed. Grace tried to explain the biology of the forest to Selfridge and Quaritch.

"There's some kind of electrochemical communication between the roots of the trees. Like the synapses between neurons. There are more connections than the human brain. Get it?" she paused. "It's a global network and the Na'vi can access it. They can upload and download data, memories...at sites like the one you just destroyed."

Selfridge nodded in apparent understanding and for a moment Grace and Jake thought they'd got through to him. Until...

"What the hell have you people been smoking out there?" Selfridge cackled. "They're just trees!"

"You need to wake up, Parker," Grace said. "The wealth of this world isn't in the ground. It's all around us. The Na'vi know that and they're fighting to defend it. If you want to share this world with them, you need to understand them."

Quaritch, though, smiled. Pointing to Jake's intel as a vital source of understanding. He turned to a monitor playing back part of Jake's videolog.

"They're not going to give up their home or make a deal," Jake was saying on-screen. "There's nothing that we have that they want."

Jake watched with mounting dread as his words condemned the people he'd grown to love. Grace, speechless, put her hand on his shoulder.

>

Having dismissed the science team, Quaritch spoke privately to Selfridge about his planned attack.

"I'll do it with minimal casualties to the indigenous. I'll drive them out with gas first. It'll be humane. More or less."

Fiddling with the lump of Unobtanium, Selfridge bent his head in thought for a moment before making his decision. His eyes glazed as he imagined the fortune he'd make from mining the land beneath Hometree, giving the instruction to attack.

An hour later Jake, Norm and Grace were sitting in the Bio Lab, checking out the monitor and discussing their situation, when Trudy burst in.

She told them of Selfridge and Quaritch's plans. They were leaving immediately to hit Hometree.

Grace and Jake sped to the Operations Centre, where Parker surveyed the airfield, watching crews of troopers swarm over a legion of gunships.

Their pleas weren't enough. As far as Parker could see, there was plenty of trees the Na'vi could move to. Jake had one hour to get them to evacuate.

Jake and Grace came round in Hometree.

Neytiri called to her parents as she watched Jake pull himself to his feet.

Jake asked Eytukan if he could address the Na'vi and, when he did so, revealed the true nature of his arrival on Pandora. The people gasped in horror as they heard that the 'Sky People' intended to destroy Hometree.

A murmur of fear and anger rippled through the crowd, but worse was to come.

Jake lowered his gaze. "They sent me here to learn your ways. So one day I could bring this message and you would believe it."

Neytiri rounded on him, unable to believe her ears.

"Look, at first it was just orders," Jake said in anguished tones, placing his hands on her shoulders. "Then everything changed. I fell in love with the forest, the Omaticaya and with you."

Neytiri pulled away from his grasp, her eyes brimming with tears.

"I trusted you," she cried, shaking with rage and pain.

"You will never be one of the people!" She yelled in Na'vi as she walked away.

Jake and Grace were now the enemy. Eytukan ordered Tsu'tey to bind the pair. He did so, and then let out a terrifying war-cry which was echoed by the clan.

>

As Jake and Grace knelt helplessly in the dirt, the sky outside darkened with a flotilla of Scorpion gunships, flying low over the rainforest. Leading the formation was one, much larger ship, a 41.15 metres long monster Dragon Gunship.

Inside the cockpit. Quaritch sat next to the pilot of the Dragon, surveying the world below like a modern-day Napoleon.

"Group leader to formation. Time on target: one minute," he said.

"Roger that. Stay on heading three zero" responded a navigator.

On the ground Jake and Grace were now lashed to a primitive scaffold in front of Hometree.

They both cried out desperately, warning the natives to save themselves by running into the forest. But the clan held fast, watching as the gunships loomed into view.

"You have to leave. Run!" Jake and Grace yelled, but to no avail. The Na'vi were nothing if not courageous and they held fast, bracing themselves for the onslaught of these alien monsters.

"That is one big damn tree," said Quaritch, surveying the scene. "Get us in close. I want them to feel the rotors."

The down-blast from the rotors created a whirlwind of flying leaves and debris, but still the Omaticaya didn't move.

"Take the *Ikran*! Attack from above!" Eytukan yelled to Tsu'tey, who gathered his hunters and ran up the tree toward the *Ikran* eyrie.

Quaritch stared in awe at the gigantic tree, its people still inside. Then, noticing a structure at the entrance he scaled the image up to see Jake and Grace tied up. Two Omaticaya warriors held knives to their throats.

Quaritch smiled at the image, mocking the attempts of diplomacy before ordering his people to get the job done – he wanted this to be quick.

The gunner turned his rocket launchers into position and, on the order of Quaritch, the inside of Hometree erupted with multiple explosions of teargas.

Confused villagers ran left and right to avoid the smoking canisters, coughing and gagging as they ran.

Enraged, Eytukan gave the signal to attack. The remaining hunters, mounted on Direhorses, bravely fired at the gunships with their longbows. Neytiri drew her bow and aimed straight at the Dragon's cockpit.

Quaritch shook his head in disbelief as the arrows rained down on the gunship's windshield, leaving traces of toxins smeared on the glass.

It was time to turn up the heat, he ordered his men to switch incendiaries.

The gunners obeyed orders and launched the missiles which hit the base of Hometree, sending it up in flames.

>

Panic ensued as missile after missile hit the target. The villagers poured out of Hometree screaming as explosions ripped through their dwelling.

High up in the trunk, Tsu'tey and his hunters leapt rapidly from branch to branch, heading for the eyrie, barely staying ahead of the fireball engulfing the tree. Flames roared up the inside of the trunk like a chimney, sending the totem and skull of Toruk crashing to the floor.

Eytukan ordered everyone into the forest.

Tied to the post, Jake saw a terrified Neytiri walk serenely out of the entrance. He called to her, but she stared at him with hatred and ran off into the forest.

"Oh my God!" screamed Grace as missiles took out the tree's central columns, rocking it to the core. The massive tree was about to come crashing down on top of them.

Then, out of the smoke, Mo'at appeared. She stumbled towards them, holding a knife.

"Mo'at, no!" pleaded Grace as the *Tsahik* placed the blade against Jake's throat.

Mo'at's eyes were filled with horror but also something stronger - faith.

"If you are one of us, help us!" she said, cutting Jake free and moving on to Grace.

Grace, Jake and Mo'at managed to jump down from the scaffold and run into the forest. The gunships, including Trudy's Samson, hovered, watching Hometree burn and awaiting orders.

A voice sounded on Trudy's radio, telling her to switch missiles. She flicked a switch on her joystick, her finger poised over the red trigger.

Missiles streamed down from the gunships. An explosion knocked Jake, Grace and Mo'at from their feet. They got up and kept running.

Jake dragged Grace and Mo'at over a felled tree, ducking down as parts of the tree fell around them. Explosion after explosion rocked Hometree, snapping the giant columns. Huge splinters of wood shot through the forest, killing many of the Omaticaya. Leaves rained down from the dying tree and the banshees took flight from the eyrie. Tsu'tey and the other hunters just had time to mount and fly off.

In her cockpit Trudy was sickened by the scene. She hadn't signed up for this. Flicking the cap over her missile trigger she banked out of formation and headed for home.

The flaming columns eventually gave way and, with a thunderous creak, the majestic tree began to topple. The Omaticaya fled as fast as they could but such an enormous tree covered a huge amount of terrain and the slowest clan members met their end beneath the heavy branches. Neytiri just managed to dodge an enormous log which fell just feet from her head. Then there was silence.

"Good work people. First round's on me tonight," smiled Quaritch, taking a sip of his coffee and patting the Dragon's pilot on the back.

>

ARMING AREA - ZONE 6

On the ground the eerie silence seemed to last an eternity, but what followed was far worse. The forest erupted with the grieving wails and screams of a thousand Omaticaya. They wept for the home and the family they had lost. Pulling herself to her feet, Neytiri's eyes were wide with horror. All that remained of Hometree was a flaming stump and ravished earth. All around, her people lay injured and dying. Suddenly she let out a wail. Eytukan, her father, lay twisted on the ground, his torso pierced by a jagged sliver of wood. Neytiri flung herself down at his side, sobbing amid the smoke and flame-filled forest.

"Daughter, take my bow," rasped Eytukan, weakly pushing his longbow toward Neytiri. "Protect the People," he whispered. His eyes closed.

At that instant, Jake, who had been searching for Neytiri, found her crumpled over her father's corpse, sobs racking her body.

He murmured his apologies, reaching out to her.

Neytiri jumped as if scalded by his touch. She sprang to her feet, tears streaming down her face.

"Get away! Never come back!" She screamed.

In the Link Room at Hell's Gate, the science team watched the scene on monitors. Most turned their heads, some wept. Even Parker Selfridge, who'd joined them with his troopers, seemed shocked by the sheer scale of the terror they had wreaked on the forest and the people. Then he seemed to wake up.

"Pull the plug!" he told the troopers.

Max protested wildly as one of the Sec-Ops team pushed the button on Grace's link.

For the second time Norm tried to intervene on behalf of his friends. This time he punched a trooper, but two more jumped him and another trooper pressed the power button on Jake's link unit.

Grace slumped to the floor in the forest. Her concerned students gathered round her and tried to revive her. They managed to get her onto a make-shift stretcher and join the stream of Omaticaya, headed by Neytiri and Mo'at, making their way up the hillside to find refuge. Jake however was on his own. Rejected by Neytiri and knowing he'd betrayed the clan he wandered in a dazed state amid the devastation until his unit powered off and he too fell to the floor.

Opening his eyes in the link he found himself violently pulled from the gel bed and escorted off to a holding cell. In his confusion he could hear Grace shouting "murderer!" at Selfridge as the troopers arrested her and carried her off. >

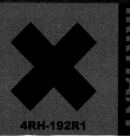

4RH-192R1

IRRITANT

NO/REF/NR: 16-987
LOT: TR-99078:09
EXP: ER3458X
RME SUPP: SMALESTSS

WARNING

1. An electro-optic transportation warning system for examining a location in an intended path of a moving vehicle for a blockage when that location is not within the line-of-sight of the moving vehicle comprising (i) a laser transceiver means to transmit a laser signal from the moving vehicle through air (ii) a first fiberoptic coupling means to collect the laser signal through a collimating means

Norm, Grace and Jake were detained in the lock-up. They sat in silence. Too wired to sleep, too emotionally drained to move. Late that night the scrape of wheels on tile made them look up. Trudy entered the room, pushing a stainless steel trolley.

The trio held their breath as the guard let her in.

"What's going on, brother?" she greeted the guard.

He droned a greeting, allowing her to push her trolley into the room.

"Personally, I don't feel these tree hugging traitors deserve steak," she said.

The guard bent down to inspect the plates and immediately felt the cold metal of Trudy's pistol pressing behind his ear. She forced the surprised guard to the floor and pistol-whipped him unconscious.

Within seconds she'd called in Max to release her friends from the cell with his key card and all five were on their way back up the utility corridor running the length of the base.

Trudy handed Norm a pistol and a mask and the pair sprinted off, out of an airlock and onto the airfield.

As they too reached the airlock, Jake asked Max to stay behind - needing someone he could trust on the inside.

Trudy and Norm reached the Samson and began racing through pre-flight checks.

Jake and Grace, however, had been spotted crossing the airfield.

A Sec-Ops member alerted the Colonel. Seeing the fleeing group on-screen, the Colonel grabbed a machine gun from a nearby trooper and ran for the airfield.

Holding his breath as he had no mask, he fired on the helicopter and its passengers. When the machine gun ran out of ammunition he switched to a pistol, but to his frustration the Samson sped up and out of range.

Jake and Norm hi-fived in delight as they climbed away from the base and out of danger.

An elated-sounding Trudy asked if all of her passengers were OK.

"Yeah, baby! We're all good," Jake grinned.

He looked at Grace, and then froze. Grace had removed her hand from inside her shirt and was examining it. It was covered in blood.

"This is going to ruin my whole day," she groaned.

For the rest of the journey Jake urged Grace to apply pressure to her wound while Grace tried to convince Jake that it wasn't serious.

The Samson flew deep into the Hallelujah Mountains to the research station. Jake activated Norm's link to allow his avatar, which had been left there, to attach the station to the helicopter with wires.

Trudy then flew the station, with Norm standing on top and Jake and Grace inside, to the tree of souls. The flux vortex was strongest there and Jake had a hunch the Omaticaya would be there.

Jake did his best to make Grace comfortable, keeping her warm and giving her an injection to relieve her pain. Jake looked at her blood-soaked abdomen and tried to keep her positive.

He told her that he'd get her help from the people to save her.

"Why would they help us?" she replied.

Unable to answer, Jake looked away and waited for touchdown.

>

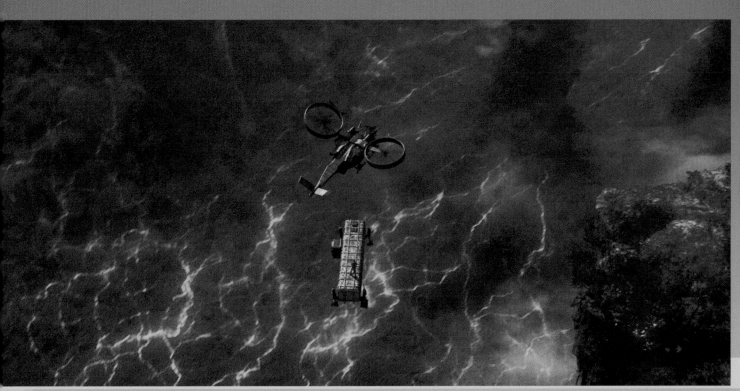

Jake was right. The Omaticaya had indeed retreated to their most sacred place looking for sanctuary. The refugees clustered around the central rock which formed a kind of altar.

A single willow, the Mother Tree, grew in the centre of the rock. Its roots spread down to the grotto floor, merging with the roots of other willows ringing the well, forming a braided mat resembling the surface of the human brain.

"Wise ancestors who live within Eywa," chanted Mo'at, from the dais. "Give us a sign."

The helicopter with its research shack, suspended beneath it, landed in a clearing near the tree.

"Tsu'tey is *Olo'eyktan* now. He's clan leader. He's not gonna let you near that place," Norm told Jake.

"I've got to try," Jake replied, climbing into the link bed as Norm began flicking buttons.

He coughed and sat up, back in his avatar once more. He was in a post-Armageddon wasteland, scorched beyond recognition. Ash from the great inferno of Hometree fell on him like filthy snow.

'I'm an outcast. Betrayer. Alien,' he thought. Looking around at hell on Pandora he realised he was going to have to take things to a whole new level.

A screech from the sky made him look up. His banshee, bonded to him for life, flapped down in front of it. Jake stepped to it, stroking its head fondly. The creature nudged his chest like a horse. But the mission they were about to go on wouldn't be to the banshee's liking.

He jumped astride the great beast and soared into the sky, thinking about the insanity of his next move.

Jake flew back to the mountain ridge where he and Neytiri had first encountered the Great Leonopteryx - *Toruk*.

He flew for an hour without a sighting but suddenly, there it was, gliding effortlessly through the air. 'It's the baddest cat in the sky,' thought Jake. 'Nothing attacks it. Which is why it never looks up.'

This was the theory Jake worked on as he approached *Toruk* stealthily from above and behind. He soared noiselessly down on his banshee until they were almost directly above the great beast, and then Jake dismounted and dropped like a stone onto *Toruk's* back.

That afternoon at the Tree of Souls, the Omaticaya were still praying. Their voices merged as they sang of loss, grief and a yearning for deliverance. In Na'vi, Neytiri sang along. "We are all seeds of the Great Tree..."

A great shadow crossed her face and she looked up. Her eyes widened in terror.

A terrible cry echoed through the air turning all eyes skyward. The huge mass of *Toruk* blotted out the sun. Backlit by the sun, it was an awesome and terrifying sight. People scattered left and right as it came to land among them. Then they saw Jake. Riding high on its shoulders, plugged-in to its antenna. The Omaticaya watched in amazement as Toruk lowered its body and Jake dismounted.

"*Toruk Makto!*" gasped Mo'at. Her words were echoed by the crowd as Jake stroked the animal's flank and stepped towards Neytiri.

"I See you," she uttered.

"I See you," replied Jake, his voice a hoarse whisper.

The emotion between them was powerful and pure. Neytiri's eyes brimmed with tears as Jake took her face in his hands and stared into her enormous, yellow eyes.

"I was afraid, Jake. For my people," Neytiri's voice cracked with hope. "I'm not anymore."

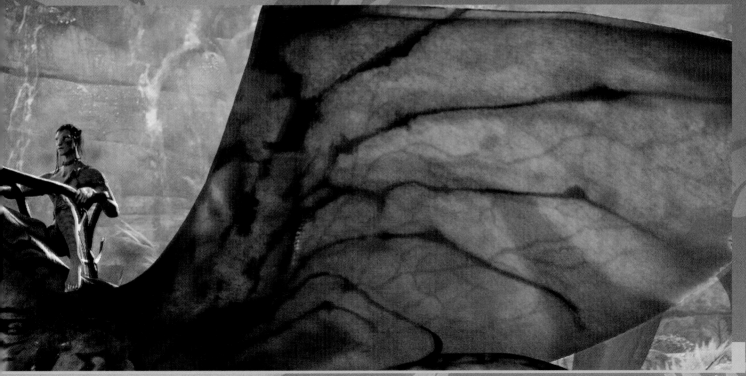

Jake took a deep breath and headed for the dais where Mo'at and Tsu'tey stood. Tsu'tey stared at Jake with a mixture of fear and incomprehension.

"Tsu'tey, son of Ateyo. I stand before you, ready to serve the Omaticaya People." Jake said solemnly.

Neytiri joined her mother and took her hand.

"You are *Olo'eyctan*, and you are a great warrior." Jake continued to Tsu'tey. "I can't do this without you."

There was a pause before Tsu'tey placed his hand on Jake's heart. He agreed to fly with the new *Toruk Makto*. Jake smiled at the warrior who was now his ally, but he had not finished. He turned to Mo'at. He pleaded with her to help save Grace, to which the Matriarch agreed.

Jake returned to the research centre in his avatar body and carried Grace out, her face ashen beneath the mask that enabled her to breathe. Norm followed with Grace's avatar in his arms.

"Look where we are Grace," Jake told his friend. Her eyes fluttered open and she looked wonderingly up at *Eywa*, Mother Tree.

Mo'at directed Jake and Norm to lay Grace and her avatar next to each other on the dais.

"The Great Mother may choose to save all that she is, in this body," she indicated Grace's avatar.

Jake gaped, realising that Mo'at was saying Grace's spirit might pass forever into her Na'vi form.

"She must pass through the Eye of Eywa, and return. But Jakesully," Mo'at warned, "she is very weak."

The Omaticaya began to sway and chant rhythmically, each person's arms reaching out and touching the shoulders of the person beside them. Mo'at stood chanting amongst the tendrils of the Mother Tree.

"May the spiral of the lives of the People fill her. May her spirit remain a longer time in her body," she chanted.

"Help her, Eywa," the clan repeated hypnotically.

The Mother Tree's roots branched out and entwined with Grace's avatar's hair, spreading over both bodies.

Suddenly Mo'at stopped. Grace's eyes flew open as she desperately tried to anchor herself to life.

"I'm with her Jake," she said in an amazed whisper. "She's real!"

Jake watched on as the chanting built to a crescendo and then died suddenly. The Mother Tree and surrounding willows, which had been glowing lighter and lighter, dulled. In that instant Grace breathed her last breath.

"Her wounds were too great, it was not enough time. She is with Eywa now," Mo'at said.

Neytiri gently removed Grace's mask. Jake sank down in despair. His friend and mentor was gone.

The People watched curiously to see what Jake would do next, feeling his pain. After several moments, he raised his head, took Neytiri's hand and turned to Tsu'tey.

"With your permission," he bowed, "I will speak now. You would honour me by translating."

So Jake, with Tsu'tey translating into Na'vi, began to rally the clan.

"The Sky People have sent us a message, that they can take whatever they want," he shouted, "and no-one can stop them. But we will send *them* a message!"

He paused to take in the expectant faces.

"You ride out, as fast as the wind can carry you. Tell the other clans to come. Tell them *Toruk Makto* calls to them. Fly now, my Brothers and Sisters and we will show the Sky People that this...this is our land."

Tus'tey's bloodcurdling war-cry was echoed by the entire clan. Jake took Neytiri's hand and ran to the Leonopteryx, vaulting onto its back and pulling her up behind. With a thunder of wings, they were gone.

Turn to page 90 for the final part of the story.

AVATAR QUIZ:
PHASE THREE

Is your brain as brilliantly active and healthy as Jake Sully's? Could you live happily ever after among the Na'vi? Pass the ultimate test here and check your final score on Page 108.

1. Who is this RDA employee and what is his job?

2. Why is it difficult to locate the Tree of Souls?

3. What is the full name of this military vehicle?

4. What did Quaritch promise Jake in return for intelligence he provided?

5. How do the Na'vi communicate and bond with animals and what is the Na'vi word for this process?

6. What do the Na'vi believe happens to their people when they die?

7. Why does the RDA want the Omaticaya to relocate?

8. What is the Na'vi name for this creature and how does it translate in English?

9. What is the English translation of these Na'vi words and phrases?
a: Skxawng b:Taronyu
c: Eywa Ngahu

10. What does an individual who tames The Great Leonopteryx become?

11. Who killed this woman and how?

12. What is this creature and what is its function?

PANDORA LOCATIONS: THE HALLELUJAH MOUNTAINS ⌐

The scientists working out of Hell's Gate Colony are pioneering human exploration on Pandora. Their mission is to study the biology, geology and zoology of this Earth-like moon and specifically learn about the indigenous population, called Na'vi, via the Avatar DNA infusion program.

The Hallelujah Mountains create a jaw-dropping spectacle for visitors to Pandora. They are a series of floating islands of rock shrouded in mist that circulate slowly in the magnetic currents of the Flux Vortex, like icebergs at sea. They cast huge, shifting shadows on the land below.

Overgrown with foliage, straggly beards of vines hang down beneath the mountains. Their sides are sheer cliffs down which waterfalls stream. The water disperses into spray which then evaporates. It condenses on other floating mountains renewing the water cycle.

Huge outcroppings of Unobtanium rip loose from the surface of Pandora and float in the magnetic vortices, often becoming tangled in the vines hanging from the Hallelujah Mountains. These create beanstalk-esque paths to the least accessible peaks including The Mountain of Truth or *Mons Veritatis*, one of the highest peaks, hovering 2,600m above the ground. Mountain Banshees roost on this mountain and would-be hunters much reach the summit in order to take the rite of passage and capture and bond with their *Ikran*.

This entire area is sacred to the Na'vi, which poses a problem for humans wishing to mine them for their mineral wealth. In any case the magnetic fields of the Flux Vortex render most weaponry and detection instruments useless in this region.

THE TREE OF SOULS⏎

The Tree of Souls, Mother Tree or *Vitraya Ramunong*, is a gigantic willow-like tree, which, as the closest connection to Eywa on Pandora, holds extreme spiritual significance for the Na'vi.

It lies amidst the Hallelujah Mountains, right at the heart of Pandora's Flux Vortex. This makes it difficult for outsiders to find. Further protection is afforded by the incredible series of natural rock arches which surround and encase it. Its exact location is on top of a large deposit of Unobtanium, at the centre of a basin - sometimes referred to as The Well of Souls - measuring roughly 60 metres in diameter.

Besides offering the Na'vi a direct connection to Eywa, The Tree of Souls also functions as a way for Eywa to interact with the world through its seeds or Woodsprite (Atokorina'). The tree has the capability to connect directly to the nervous system of all living things via its roots, and is not limited to the neural hair braid or 'queue' that Pandoran beings possess.

The Omaticaya even use the tree to transfer the minds of humans whose bodies are failing, into their perfect Avatar forms. Grace Augustine was too weak to make the leap and instead passed away and became one with Eywa, but Jake Sully successfully made the transition, making his Na'vi Avatar his true body forever.

The destruction of the Tree of Souls would prove devastating to the Na'vi as a whole, creating a cultural and religious void that would decimate the race entirely. It is because of this, that Colonel Quaritch based his attack strategy around the tree, planning to bomb it into oblivion, as he had done with Hometree.

PANDORA: NA'VI WEAPONS ⌐

Na'vi weapons may be more humble than those wielded by the human colonists, but they are devastating and lethal in their efficiency.

BANSHEE XBOW

DESCRIPTION: Shaped in wood from Hometree, this bow weighs 3.7 kilos and is almost 3 metres high. Fashioned in honor of the Direhorse, these exquisite bows are traditionally handed down through the generations, and become powerful symbols of survival and tradition.

FUNCTION: This ranged bow is primarily designed for ceremonies by clan elders, but it is crafted to the peak of Na'vi design and functions perfectly in hunt or battle.

HUNTING ARROWS

DESCRIPTION: Made from an oversized bone head, bound to a reed shaft with natural glues and fibres. Fletching is added in feather in two styles, lashed with plant fiber or animal sinew. The other is a spiral fletch wrapped around the shaft that causes the arrow to spin and be more accurate. The fletching is trimmed to ensure rapid flight. Sizes range from 1.5m to 2.5m.

FUNCTION: Na'vi Hunting Arrows are short ranged weapons designed to function in a jungle environment. Although neurotoxin is used on arrow heads to subdue the large fauna present on Pandora, it is not needed for smaller quarry such as fish, due to the huge size of the arrow point.

CEREMONIAL BOW

DESCRIPTION: Made from horn, the bow weighs around 3. 4 kilos and is almost 3 metres high. Hunters decorate the weapon with banshee motifs and markings to personalize it.

FUNCTION: Primarily designed to be used in battle from the back of a banshee in flight. The very light threads on the string can help determine wind direction for a stationary shot. The low hand grip and shorter base of the bow allows for ease of movement while the design ensures the lower part of the bow stays clear of the banshee.

HUNTERS BOLA

DESCRIPTION: This is a rope, weighted at each end with hard polished seeds.

FUNCTION: A simple entanglement weapon used for hunting, clan members are taught to use it from a very early age. In the right hands it can bring down a large animal from a distance of 10 metres.

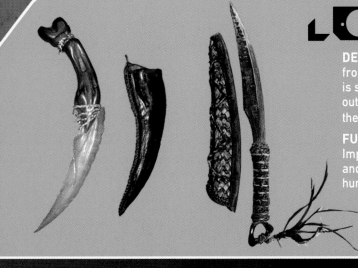

NA'VI HUNTING KNIFE

DESCRIPTION: The blade, fashioned from the wing claw of an *Ikran* (banshee), is semi-translucent. Handles are made out of wood and are customised by the individual.

FUNCTION: The knife is a very Important part of the culture of the Na'vi and is used by all members of a clan for hunting, skinning, whittling or combat.

NA'VI TOOLS & ACCESSORIES⤶

The Na'vi have all manner of ingenious devices to help them with daily life on Pandora. Here are a few:

 NA'VI BASKET

DESCRIPTION: Woven from organic materials such as wood and flax-like leaves, this basket incorporates a strap which rests on the head, allowing the clan member to transport its contents easily and securely on his or her back.

FUNCTION: Transporting water, food or raw materials from or to the clan.

NA'VI HAND BLADE

DESCRIPTION: Made of Animal bone hewn in a semi-circle this is held in two-hands.

FUNCTION: Chopping of food, animal flesh and other small materials.

 NA'VI JARS

DESCRIPTION: Fashioned in stone.

FUNCTION: Used to hold all manner of Na'vi essentials. Ceremonial jars also exist for particular rituals and rites of passage such as the Arachnoid Jar, used to capture the scorpion-like arachnoid for a warrior initiation.

 NA'VI LANTERNS

DESCRIPTION: Fashioned from bio-luminescent matter found within the jungle, these glow come nightfall.

FUNCTION: Lighting within enclosed spaces such as the interior of Hometree.

FIRE PIT

DESCRIPTION: Fashioned out of rock placed within woven wood on ring of stones.

FUNCTION: General cooking and heating of liquids.

PANDORA: WILDLIFE

From arboreal herbivores such as the ape-like Prolemuris, to the uber-carnivorous Leonopteryx, fiercest predator on the planet, the creatures of Pandora never cease to strike awe into the hearts of the indigenous and colonial peoples.

MOUNTAIN BANSHEE – *IKRAN*

The Mountain Banshee dwells in a rookery atop the Hallelujah Mountains. Once captured it will form a bond with its hunter that lasts a lifetime and will fly with no-one else. Like its smaller cousin, the Forest Banshee, which lives in tree-top eyries, the Mountain Banshee is highly adapted for flight.

Specially developed muscles along the breastbone allow for the powerful strokes needed to achieve lift. Xenobiologists continue to study the aerodynamics of the banshee. It is believed all of Pandora's flying animals take advantage of gravity that is lower than Earth's and the increased air density, achieving more impetus per wing flap.

The downside is that the denser air is harder to move through, and requires highly-efficient streamlining to achieve high flight speeds.

GREAT LEONOPTERYX – *TORUK*

Great Leonopteryx - *Toruk* King predator of the sky, this red and yellow coloured flyer has a wing span of 25 metres and is several times larger than its main prey, the Mountain Banshee. The beauty and nobility of the Leonopteryx gave the species a central place in Na'vi lore and culture. It is celebrated in dance, song, and with elaborate totems that symbolize both the fear and respect given to the creature. Indeed, the Leonopteryx is crucial to the Na'vi's sense of destiny.

This creature's name in Na'vi translates as 'Last Shadow', as its preferred method of attack is from above. Therefore, the last thing its prey sees before death is *Toruk's* shadow.

Despite superior binocular vision, *Toruk* is unable to see directly above itself, a weakness Jake Sully exploits when attempting to bond with it. Speedy and territorial, this beast has only bonded with a hunter six times since time began. The hunter who tames it becomes *Toruk Makto* and has the ear and respect of every Na'vi clan.

HAMMERHEAD TITANOTHERE – *ANGTSIK*

Like a six-legged rhinoceros, only twice the size, this tough, stalking carnivore lives in herds and has signature bone projections on its low slung head. It uses its hammerhead in attack or defence.

THANATOR – *PALULUKAN*

Pandora's most fearsome land-based predator, this 6-metre long, black pantheresque killing machine, hunts alone. It has an armoured head and a venomous tail making it lethal from every side. Its distensible jaw allows for maximum tooth extension and even the Na'vi, renowned for their courage and tolerance of all living things, are shaken by its approach.

VIPERWOLF – *NANTANG*

This sleek and sly hunter has evolved to allow it to run long distances through the jungle. Thanks to opposable thumbs it climbs like a monkey and uses razor like fangs to rip its prey to pieces. It is nocturnal and hunts in packs.

STINGBAT – *RITI*

With its metre-wide wingspan, glass-like fangs and deadly sharp tail, this flying omnivore can inflict injury or death on most enemies. It can, however, fall prey to Forest Banshees. Those who do not see it as a threat - such as the Na'vi - see a subdued, docile animal.

HEXAPEDE – *YERIK*

This gentle herbivore is deer-like in demeanour and represents a major food source for the Na'vi. Gentle and unassuming, its bright blue hue and translucent headdress can keep it camouflaged against the Pandoran landscape at night or by day.

DIRE HORSE – *PA'LI*

Vaguely horse-like in appearance, but with long necks, antennae, armoured backs, small heads and six legs, these creatures are herbivores, supping nectar from flowers. When wild, the animals move together in a loose herd through the forests, feeding on tree bark and shrubs. Many Direhorses are tamed to aid their riders in the hunt and in battle. To bond with a Direhorse, a Na'vi must mount the animal and connect their neural queue to the animal's antennae.

GATHERED AT THE SACRED TREE OF SOULS, THE CLAN CHEERED AS JAKE AND NEYTIRI SOARED INTO THE SKY ON *TORUK*. A FEW HOURS AGO THEIR SITUATION HAD SEEMED DESPERATE. THEIR CHIEF LAY DEAD, HOMETREE WAS NO MORE; THEIR VERY EXISTENCE WAS UNDER THREAT FROM THE MALEVOLENT 'SKY PEOPLE'.

Now, hope had returned in the unlikely form of Jake, who had mastered *Toruk*, the Great Leonopteryx and had flown back to them.

The Omaticaya heard Jake's words and rode and flew out to the far corners of Pandora in search of support for their fight against the Sky People.

Jake, Neytiri, Tsu'tey and the hunters visited the horse clans of the plains and the Ikran people of the Eastern Sea. The power of *Toruk Makto* was such that all Na'vi clans were happy to follow Jake's bidding and by dawn the next day thousands of Na'vi were swelling the ranks of the Omaticaya, gathered at the Tree of Souls. They came by banshee, by Direhorse and on foot and when the clearing around the Mother Tree was rammed to capacity, they camped in the forest. An awesome army.

Meanwhile, back at Hell's Gate, Quaritch was amassing his own, formidable force.

The Colonel faced his troops in the commissary. All base personnel were crowded into the room for his pre-mission briefing. Somehow today his scar seemed more vivid. A reminder of the ferocious enemy they were facing.

He looked round the room. "There's an aboriginal horde out there massing for an attack," he continued. He leant over and started the 3D graphics projector and an aerial view of the area around the Tree of Souls appeared on the screen behind him. While the habitat was blue and green, the infrared camera showed life forms in yellow. The map was more yellow than blue.

"Now, these orbital images tell me that the hostiles' numbers have gone from a few hundred to well over two thousand in one day, and more are pouring in. In a week's time, there could be twenty thousand of them. At that point, they'll overrun our perimeter. Well that's not going to happen."

Quaritch's tone became steely. Their opponents had gotten stronger, but he was still confident of succeeding.

They would launch a pre-emptive attack, to take the swelling horde of Na'vi by surprise.

Quaritch watched to see if his speech had had the desired impact. It had. At this ultimate soundbite, fear transformed to hatred in the eyes of the miners and troopers.

"The hostiles believe that this mountain stronghold of theirs is protected by their..." he paused and sniggered, "their deity. When we destroy it, we will blast a crater in their racial memory so deep that they won't come within a thousand klicks of this place ever again!"

The room erupted in bawdy cheers. Troopers Wainfleet and Fike glanced at each other and smiled grimly. They were psyched-up and ready for a fight.

>

Holed up in the Bio-Lab, Max switched on a monitor and called his friends at the research station.

Jake, Norm and Trudy tuned in as his face appeared on-screen. Max spoke quickly in case the channel was not secure and someone was listening in.

"It's full mobilization. They're rigging the Valkyrie shuttle as a bomber. They've got these huge pallets of mine explosives."

Max warned that the assault would start at 6am the next day. A noise behind him made him sign off abruptly, leaving Norm, Jake and Trudy to take in the news. Jake was deep in thought.

"I have 15 clans out there. Over 2000 warriors," said Jake, looking up at his friends, his gaze intense. "We know these mountains. We fly them. You fly them," he pointed to Trudy.

He recalled how Trudy's helicopter hadn't been able to cope in the mountains, how its equipment had gone haywire in flight - which would give Jake and his army an advantage.

Norm and Trudy warned that Quaritch would head straight to the Tree of Souls. If he did, the fight would be over.

Jake nodded. "Then I guess we'd better stop him," he said.

Later that evening Jake climbed back into the link and reinhabited his avatar. He headed straight for the Tree of Souls - The Mother Tree - and knelt among its beautiful tendrils, placing his hands on its roots.

He took hold of his neural queue and gently connected it to one of the tendrils, "I need to give you a head's up."

Jake looked up towards the top of the trunk and opened his heart.

He implored the tree to look into Grace's memories and realise that the planet he came from was different to Pandora - humans had killed their Mother and would fight relentlessly until they'd done the same here.

There was a soft padding behind Jake but he was so lost in the moment he didn't hear it.

"...unless we stop them."

Woodsprites began floating down from up in the tree.

Neytiri, who had come to find Jake, touched him on the shoulder and helped him to his feet.

"Our Great Mother does not take sides, Jake," she said gently. "She protects only the balance of life."

Neytiri took Jake's face in her hands and looked at him lovingly. He returned her gaze.

"It was worth a try." he whispered, leaning in so that his forehead touched hers.

For a long time they held each other. Basking in one last moment of peace.

>

At zero six hundred hours exactly, the fleet of gunships, shuttles and Scorpion and Samson helicopters left Hell's Gate. The formation was an awe-inspiring sight as it flew through the Hallelujah Mountains towards its destination.

Quaritch stood in the cockpit of the Dragon Gunship, enjoying the view, and his morning cup of coffee.

The Group Leader sounded over the radio. Upon entering the Flux Vortex he ordered the troop to switch to manual flight mode.

Several kilometres away a huge flock of banshees approached, ridden by warriors including Tsu'tey and Neytiri and headed by Jake, who rode *Toruk*. The warriors were decorated with striking war paint, their hair braided with beads and feathers.

Jake, Tsu'tey and Neytiri wore microphones around their throats to allow them to communicate with each other, once in battle.

Quaritch, calm and confident of success, ordered his team to be done by dinner.

The Dragon approached a clearing and landed. Behind it the Samsons touched down, disgorging troops while the Scorpions hovered protectively overhead.

Wainfleet led a team of troopers driving AMP Suits. On his signal they abseiled from the Dragon on wires and stormed into the forest.

Quaritch radioed from the Dragon, which was now on its way to the Tree of Souls, warning his gun crews to be alert. The full formation moved slowly underneath the floating mountains of rock.

"Come on, boy. Come on out and show me what you got," Quaritch breathed to Jake, his invisible enemy.

Above the gunships, hidden from sight by incredible camouflage, the hunters and their banshees clung to the rocks, waiting for the right moment to launch their ambush.

Down in the jungle Wainfleet caught a sudden movement on the screen in his AMP Suit. Ghostly thermal signatures moved across the display.

"Hold position," he ordered. "We got movement out there. Five hundred metres."

Behind him Fike and the other troopers stopped. Suddenly, a chilling sound echoed through the forest. The ululating war cries of untold Na'vi.

The troopers scanned the treeline, spooked. They were unable to tell where the noise was coming from.

Wainfleet and the troopers and AMP Suits cautiously moved forward into formation, weapons raised, breath collectively held.

He waited for approval to fire but the Flux Vortex prevented Quaritch from hearing or seeing what was happening below. For the troopers below this was a costly delay. The earth began to tremble with the thundering hooves of 300 mounted Na'vi warriors and Norm, who rode with his gun held aloft.

>

A similar clash was about to take place hundreds of miles above the action in the forest.

Quaritch ordered the pilot of Valkyrie 1-6 to lower its ramp, as troopers readied the racks of mining explosives to be dropped, on the Tree of Souls.

Seeing the shuttle and gunships home into view Jake urged *Toruk* downwards. The enormous flock of banshees followed. Hunters crouched on their backs, screeching war cries.

Jake was the first to reach the gunships. At his bidding, *Toruk* grabbed one of the Scorpion helicopters in its claws, whirled it round as if it were a tiny insect and flung it into the side of one of the mountains, where it exploded in a ball of flame.

Tsu'tey's first arrow pierced the windshield of another Scorpion, taking out the pilot and causing it to plummet from the skies.

Neytiri, too, plunged and swooped like an angel of death, shooting arrows at the helicopters and jamming their rotas.

Quaritch ordered his pilot to swing the Dragon to its right, as he came face to face with the enemy.

On the ground the troopers at last saw their foe. The warriors were upon them.

Wainright and his men blasted the AMP Suit's guns at the approaching Na'vi.

The troopers followed his lead. Tracers riddled the jungle, blasting foliage into confetti. Charging Direhorses crashed down, flipping over under fire. Warriors were flung off into the mud, dead or mortally wounded. The withering fire steadily decimated the Na'vi ranks.

But still the natives pushed forward. They launched their arrows at full gallop. A few hit their marks. Norm managed to take out several troopers with his gun.

In the air, the Dragon banked right and began to track several banshees, opening fire and blowing them into tiny pieces. But for now, the natives seemed to have the upper hand.

Jake's Leonopteryx dived down and grabbed another Scorpion, taking the helicopter in its jaws and crushing the cockpit with one crunch. Neytiri swooped past the back of one of the gunships and struck an arrow through the heart of a trooper handling a load of explosives.

Quaritch sent his helicopter gunship squadron to lend support to the besieged troopers down in the forest. The Scorpions flew low over the trees firing on the mounted warriors. Norm's Direhorse was hit and as he ran for cover he contacted Jake by throat mic.

"Jake! Jake! You copy?" he yelled. "We're falling back. We're getting hammered."

"Copy, get out of there," Jake agreed, hearing the desperation in his friend's voice.

>

As he talked to Norm, Jake rounded the edge of one of the floating mountains and came face to face with Quaritch, in the cockpit of the Dragon.

In a flash, Jake banked left, just out of range of the gunship's missiles which blew chunks of rock from the cliff face. The chase was on. Jake slalomed violently left and right through the rocks to avoid being blown out of the sky. But *Toruk* was tiring.

"Take him out!" growled Quaritch impatiently. But just as the pilot locked his missiles on Jake, the Dragon was hit by fire from one of its own.

It was Trudy. "Oops!" she grinned, sending another barrage of fire towards the Dragon.

Quaritch ordered a retaliatory strike, realising he was under attack from a deserter. But, as the gunship prepared to fire Trudy manoeuvred head on and fired, smashing the Dragon's windshield.

Neytiri was also in trouble. A Scorpion was pursuing her at close range through the jungle. She dove lower amid the trees, losing it, but instead flew straight into a trooper in an AMP suit.

Neytiri's banshee took a hit and fell to the ground. Neytiri screamed as she was flung from its back onto the mossy ground. She was almost knocked unconscious.

Winded and stunned, she rolled onto her back and saw the lifeless form of her banshee lying metres from her.

"Tse'zey!" she cried, staggering to it and caressing its great head. It was dead.

Neytiri looked up and saw destruction all around her. A Direhorse ran past, its body engulfed in flame. Hunters were knocked from their mounts; others lay injured, crying out in pain. The forest was an inferno. She ducked down behind the corpse of her beloved banshee, praying for deliverance.

In the sky, Tsu'tey was fighting to the death. Flying close to the rear of the huge Valkyrie shuttle - its cargo making it a lethal bomber - he leapt from his banshee onto the loading ramp. He hurled one trooper off the ramp to his death. Then he continued his assault, swinging his bow with lethal force.

Tsu'tey's bravery knew no bounds, but in the end it took just one bullet to finish him. The last trooper standing let off a single, desperate round. It hit Tsu'tey square in the chest, flinging him backwards off the ramp and down to his death. The great warrior was no more.

>

Quaritch was doggedly pursuing Trudy.

The skilful and brave pilot managed to dodge missile after missile from the huge gunship but finally one connected with her helicopter. Trudy's rotors burst into flames and she began to spin out of control.

"Rogue One is hit, I'm going in. Sorry Jake," she radioed, desperately trying to bring her helicopter safely to land. But it was no use.

Seeing his prey vulnerable, Quaritch ordered the Dragon pilot fired one last shot. A fireball engulfed Trudy's Samson, killing her instantly.

At the same time, in the jungle, the troopers felled Norm. The plucky scientist continued to fire his gun until a round blasted into his shoulder, knocking him to the ground. The link was broken and he awoke gasping in the link unit.

Dazed and confused he re-armed and stumbled out into the jungle to find the Na'vi.

"Tsu'tey, Brother do you read?" yelled Jake, hovering in the mountains astride *Toruk*. There was no answer. He tried Trudy. "Rogue One, do you copy?" he called. Again, silence. The tide had turned against the Na'vi.

Sensing the welcome whiff of victory, Quaritch ordered the bomb-rigged shuttle on to its final destination. The bomber turned and headed away from the fray, towards the Tree of Souls.

Just one of Jake's allies was still communicating.

"Jake," Neytiri rasped into her throat mic. The very air seemed to burn as she tried to breathe.

"Neytiri, I read you," Jake gasped with relief. His love was alive.

"Tse'zey's dead," she told him, peeking out from behind a tree trunk to see troopers razing the jungle with flame throwers.

"They are very close and they are many," she whispered, sinking to her heels.

Jake demanded that she did not attack, but Neytiri did not respond. He desperately ordered her to fall back but, again, there was no response.

Neytiri was no longer listening. She inhaled deeply then drew her bow and arrow and prepared to make a final stand.

Just metres away, Wainfleet and his fellow troopers, clad in their robotic AMP Suits, paused, sensing movement.

Seeing the invincible line of robots, Neytiri had second thoughts. She paused, lowered her bow and closed her eyes in defeat.

Then a herd of Hammerhead Titanotheres crashed out of the undergrowth, narrowly missing her and heading for the enemy.

As the beasts closed on them, Pike and Wainfleet shouted instructions to fall back. Bullets ricocheted off the armoured beasts without doing them the slightest harm.

The AMP Suits were cumbersome. Before Wainfleet could turn and flee, a Titanothere was upon him. It scooped him up on its huge crested head and sent him crashing into the brush. The last thing Wainfleet saw were the beast's enormous front hooves rearing up over him. He let out a bloodcurdling scream as its full weight crashed down on the AMP Suit, crushing him.

Neytiri stared in awe. All around her, Pandoran creatures of every species thundered from the undergrowth...

"Jake," she croaked into her mic, "Eywa has heard you!"

>

It was the same in the sky, anything and everything that possessed a pair of wings had come to aid the Na'vi. All kinds of birds, bats and banshees swarmed over the Scorpions knocking them out of the air.

She ran through the jungle, surrounded by Viperwolves and Titanotheres, firing arrow after arrow at the retreating troops. An almighty roar made her stop dead. A Thanator crashed into view. Neytiri hardly dared breathe. For a second the great beast and the clan princess regarded each other and then slowly, surely, the Thanator lowered itself to the ground as a sign for her to mount.

The battle for the air reignited. Boosted by the unexpected support, hunters and banshees began ripping into the Scorpions with renewed vigour until the only remaining crafts in the air were the Dragon gunship and the bomber.

The alarmed pilot warned Quaritch that the other troops were backing off. The frustrated Colonel, though, wanted to get the job done.

Jake had just moments to change the Na'vi's future. He used his tried and tested tactic, swooping on the larger craft from above. He leapt from *Toruk* and landed on top of the bomber. Firing round after round, he took out the troopers in the gun turret. Then he ran at full tilt towards the nose of the shuttle, pulling a grenade from his utility belt and removing its pin with his teeth. With one gigantic lob he hurled the grenade into the intake of the ship's turbofans.

At the same time, *Toruk* banked in a tight arc back towards Jake. As the grenade exploded, shattering the turbines and riddling the fuselage with shrapnel Jake hurled himself off into space, landing on the back of *Toruk* and reconnecting his neural queue with its antenna.

Jake and *Toruk* banked away to a safe distance. They watched the bomber slide out of control and smash into one of the stone archways protecting the Tree of Souls. The bomber exploded. Eywa was safe.

Quaritch, seeing the bomber disintegrate in front of his eyes, couldn't believe it. The pilot told the Colonel that they were leaving, but Jake had other plans for the Dragon ship.

Bringing *Toruk* back around, he performed the same crazy leap onto the gunship's wing, unpinning a grenade and sprinting towards a hatch.

"It's Sully!" Quaritch screamed, snatching the pilot's joystick and slamming it hard over.

The Dragon lurched sideways, rolling sharply and Jake was flung off his feet. His grenades missed the turbines. One bounced off the ship while the other lodged near the cockpit.

Jake was flung off the wing, but managed to cling on to the edge of a weapons pod.

The grenade blew a hole in the Dragon's hull. Toxic Pandoran air swirled inside the cockpit.

Quaritch ordered the pilot to put on his mask, grabbing one for himself and heading outside to find Jake.

Dangling by one hand as Quaritch fired at him, Jake grabbed a missile from the weapons pod with the other and hurled it into the rotor blades. Unable to hold on any longer he let go and plummeted down through the air and into the wooded canopy below. He slid from huge leaf to huge leaf to break his fall, just as Neytiri had taught him.

Looking up he saw the ship explode and fall to earth, cartwheeling to a flaming standstill nearby. Had the Na'vi really won?

The Colonel was knocked flying by the force of the explosion when the missile hit the rotor blades, but incredibly he made it to an AMP Suit in the loading bay.

>

Patting flames from his shoulder he clicked the suit into operating mode and launched himself out of the burning ship, seconds before it crashed.

The AMP Suit absorbed the shock of the fall and Quaritch immediately began crashing through the jungle in pursuit of Jake, his mortal enemy. His expression was one of crazed determination. He wanted revenge and luck was on his side.

He came across the research station. Levelling his weapon at the shack, something caught his eye. Neytiri was thundering towards him on the Thanator. Quaritch whipped round just as the black demon leapt at him. He blocked the attack with the body of his cannon and used the momentum of the Thanator against Neytiri, hurling girl and beast into a tree trunk.

Neytiri recovered from the blow and attacked again on her mount, sending the AMP Suit crashing to the ground and snapping its cannon off. The Thanator leapt onto the robot, snapping at the cockpit.

"Come to Papa," yelled Quaritch, drawing the robot's knife and stabbing the creature through the heart. It roared and collapsed, trapping Neytiri under its corpse.

Then... "Give it up Quaritch, it's over," Jake appeared from the jungle.

He lunged at the Colonel using the AMP Suit's broken cannon to parry its blows.

With a powerful jab he punched a hole in the canopy. The Colonel had no choice but to kick it out and grapple for his mask before the air killed him.

"Hey Sully, how's it feel to betray your own race?" Quaritch sneered, breathing hard in the mask.

Jake hissed at him, bearing his fangs but the Colonel had other ideas. With two strides he was at the research station. His robotic arm punched a hole straight through the wall. Inside, still in his link unit Jake's eyes fluttered open. He gasped for oxygen as the Pandoran air seeped in.

Quaritch turned his attention to Jake's avatar. He grabbed him by the hair, pulled his knife and put it to Jake's throat.

Neytiri screamed as the blade began to cut Jake. With one enormous heave she released her legs from under the Thanator. She leapt into the air, drew her bow and sent two arrows flying into Quaritch's heart. The Colonel and his robot, crashed to the ground.

"Jake," Neytiri wept, crouching over Jake's avatar. There was no response.

In an instant she realised what had happened. She leapt into the station to find Jake, in his human form, on the floor beside the link, unable to reach a mask. Taking him in her arms, she clamped it on his mouth.

"I See you," he murmured, as the oxygen revived him.

"I See you," she smiled, looking into Jake's human face with love.

Despite the substantial losses of her people, not least her father and the clan's chief warrior, Jake had gone from traitor to hero and saved the sacred planet.

The battle for Pandora was over. The Na'vi looked on as the human personnel from Hell's Gate were loaded onto shuttles back to earth. Only a few of the science team were allowed to stay, including Norm and Max.

Before leaving, Jake took one last look around the Bio-Lab.

"I'd better go, I don't want to be late for my party," he said into his video log. "It is my birthday after all. "This is Jake Sully signing off."

In the clearing, at the foot of the Tree of Souls, Mo'at and the grateful Na'vi chanted over the inert bodies of Jake and of his Na'vi avatar, just as they had done with Grace. Hundreds of woodsprites danced over the bodies. Leaning over human Jake, Neytiri gently removed his oxygen mask and kissed his eyelids, allowing him to pass through the Eye of Eywa. The Mother Tree's roots spread over his dying body. Then Neytiri moved to tend to her love. She cradled avatar Jake's face in her hands, waiting. Suddenly, the blue eyelids flew open. Jake the Omaticaya lived.

TEACH YOURSELF NA'VI

Here are a few common phrases using words from the Na'vi lexicon. Why not try them out next time you're on Pandora?

GREETINGS AND GOODBYES

Kaltxì
Hello

Oe kame nga
I See you

Kame nga
See you (casual)

Kìyevame
Good bye/See you again soon

Sìltsan txon
Good night

Eywa ngahu
Goodbye, Eywa (be) with you

BASIC CONVERSATION

Tslolam
Got it, I understand

Rutxe
Please

Irayo
Thank you

Nawm
Great, noble

Fyape lu nga?
How are you?

Srane
Yes

Kehe
No

USEFUL TO KNOW!

Swotu
Sacred place

Pizayu
Ancestor

Uniltìrantokx
Avatar/Dreamwalker body

ioang
Animal, beast

Olo'eyktan
Clan leader

'Ìnglìsì
English

Sempul
Father

Sa'nok
Mother

Tsmukan
Brother

Tsmuke
Sister

Ngay
True

Tsleng
False

Sngä'i
Begin, start

Ftang
Stop

ANSWERS

Pages 36 - 37
AVATAR QUIZ: PHASE ONE

1. TRUE

2. FALSE. Exposure to the air will kill a human in around 4 minutes.

3. FALSE. Although the Titanothere is a carnivore, the Thanator is more aggressive, agile and dangerous.

4. TRUE. Although they do drink the nectar.

5. TRUE

6. FALSE. Although knives and spears are used, they favour the bow and arrow.

7. TRUE

8. FALSE. Tsa'hik is the female, spiritual leader. Like a Shaman. Olo'eyktan is the male clan leader.

9. FALSE. The Mountain Banshee is larger and the largest predator is The Great Leonopteryx.

10. TRUE

11. FALSE. They float around in the air, suspended by magnetic force fields of the Flux Vortex.

12. TRUE

Pages 58 - 59
AVATAR QUIZ: PHASE TWO

1. C: Resources and Development Administration.

2. A: five years.

3. B: ISV Venture Star.

4. A: perform amplified versions of any human activity.

5. B: the human mind transferred into a genetically engineered body of a human/Na'vi hybrid.

6. C: Commissary.

7. B: $20 million a kilo in its unrefined state.

8. B: Parker Selfridge.

9. A: he shares his deceased twin brother's DNA.

10. C: Hell's Gate.

11. B: because the gunner rides on an unprotected, raised platform like a sitting duck.

12. A: an operational link-unit.

Pages 82 - 83
AVATAR QUIZ: PHASE THREE

1. Max Cullimore, a civilian scientist working at Hell's Gate on the Avatar Program.

2. Because it is protected from view by a series of stone arches and also lies in the middle of the magnetic field called the Flux Vortex.

3. AT-99 'Scorpion' Gunship.

4. That he will authorise an operation to repair Jake's spinal cord so he can regain use of his legs.

5. By connecting their neural queue with the antenna of the creature. It is called Tsahaylu.

6. They become one with Eywa.

7. Because Hometree sits on the largest accessible deposit of precious Unobtainium on Pandora.

8. Toruk which means Last Shadow.

9. *Skxawng* - Moron
Taronyu - Hunter
Eywa Ngahu - Goodbye, Eywa be with you.

10. Toruk Makto.

11. She was fatally injured with a shot fired by Colonel Miles Quaritch while trying to escape Hell's Gate. She died beneath the Tree of Souls and passed into Eywa being too weak to pass back into her uninjured Avatar body.

12. It is a woodsprite or Atokirina'. A seed from the sacred Tree of Souls which is a pure and sacred spirit. They are believed auspicious wherever they choose to rest. The Omaticaya Clan plants one of these seeds with the body of a deceased Na'vi, so the Na'vi's consciousness will become part of Eywa.

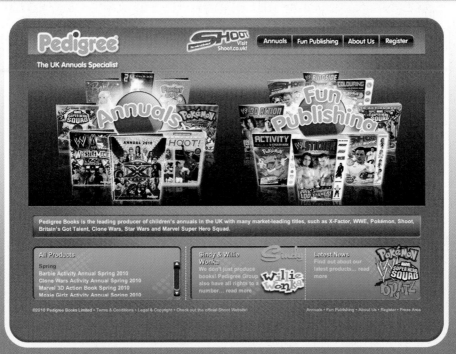

To find out more on this years Avatar Annual and all our other titles visit **www.pedigreebooks.com** where you can also order online.

Pedigree®
Always delivering more this Christmas
...for the whole family

Shoot - the voice of football. Free membership available giving you access to a monthly magazine. The only voice of football now on the web at **www.shoot.co.uk**